Buildings at Risk:

Seismic

Design

Basics

for

Practicing

Architects

a publication of the
AIA/ACSA Council on Architectural Research

AIA/ACSA Council on Architectural Research
Natural Hazards Research Program
1735 New York Avenue, NW
Washington, DC 20006

ISBN 0-935502-08-4

Deane Evans, AIA, Director - Editor
Stephanie Urban Vierra - Art Director
Pradeep Dalal - Editorial Assistant
Emily Cole - Administrative Assistant

Principal Author
   Christopher Arnold, FAIA
   Building Systems Development, Inc.
   Palo Alto, CA

Contributing Authors
   Richard Eisner, AIA, AICP
   Governor's Office of Emergency Services
   Oakland, CA

   Eric Elsesser
   Forell/Elsesser Engineers, Inc.
   San Francisco, CA

Disclaimer

This manual was prepared under Contract Number EMW-90-C-3355 with the Federal Emergency Management Agency.

The photographs, drawings, charts and other information contained in this publication have been obtained from a variety of sources including government agencies, schools of architecture, professional architects, architectural firms, and others. The AIA/ACSA Council on Architectural Research has made every reasonable effort to provide accurate information, but does not warrant, and assumes no liability for, the accuracy or completeness of the text or its fitness for any particular purpose.

Furthermore, the statements and descriptions contained in this manual do not necessarily reflect the views of the U.S. Government in general or the Federal Emergency Management Agency in particular. The U.S. Government and FEMA make no warranty, expressed or implied, and assume no responsibility for the accuracy or completeness of the information herein.

AIA/ACSA Council on Architectural Research

On May 2, 1986, the Presidents of the American Institute of Architects (AIA), and the Association of Collegiate Schools of Architecture (ACSA) signed an agreement to create a Council on Architectural Research. The purpose of the Council is to serve as a link between the schools of architecture, where significant research activity occurs, and the profession, which can utilize the results of this research in practice. The goal is to foster research which benefits both the architectural curriculum and activities within the profession of architecture, and which positively impacts the built environment and the public at large. With offices in the AIA headquarters building in Washington, DC, the AIA/ACSA Council on Architectural Research serves as a national focal point for architectural research in all its forms.

The Council is organized into a number of constituent programs which identify research priorities, initiate research projects and disseminate findings. The Council's Natural Hazards Research Program coordinates research on the effects of natural hazards on buildings and was responsible for the development of this publication.

Acknowledgements

Many people made valuable contributions to this publication, both during its actual preparation and throughout the workshops which preceded it.

We wish to first acknowledge the guidance provided by Marilyn MacCabe, the Federal Emergency Management Agency's technical representative for the project. Thanks are also due to Jane Bullock, Assistant to the Director, and Gary Johnson, Acting Chief Financial Officer, both at FEMA.

Likewise, special thanks for their unique contributions to this effort are owed to:

Henry Lagorio, University of California, Berkeley
Don Geis, AIA, Geis Design Research Assoc., Potomac, MD

Finally, the Council gratefully acknowledges support from the National Science Foundation. Under grant number 9101564, the Council was able to undertake a series of research tasks focused on expanding the current architectural knowledge base in seismic design. Results from this research were used to support and enhance the information contained in this publication.

Table of Contents

Introduction

Richard Eisner

Earthquakes are among the most frightening and devastating of natural events. The 1994 Northridge, California quake, for example, resulted in over 60 deaths, more than 5,000 injuries and over 25,000 people left homeless. In addition, 10,000 homes and businesses lost electricity, 20,000 lost gas and 50,000 were without water. Direct economic losses are estimated at over $20 billion.

And this was not the BIG ONE! It was a large (moment magnitude 6.7) but not a great earthquake, of relatively short duration (the main shock lasting roughly 15 seconds). The 1906 San Francisco quake, by contrast, was estimated as a Richter Magnitude 8.3 event, lasting 45 seconds, and the 1964 Alaska quake (a Richter 8.4) lasted over three minutes. Larger events can therefore be expected in the U.S., and they will not be confined solely to the West Coast region.

In fact, two of the severest earthquakes in U.S. history occurred east of the Rockies: one in Charleston, South Carolina in 1886; the other, a series of three shocks, in New Madrid, Missouri in 1811-12. The latter have the distinction of being the greatest series of earthquakes in U.S. history. Measuring an estimated 8.5 on the Richter scale, they sent shock waves as far west as the Rocky Mountains and as far east as Washington, D.C. and Boston. If they were to occur today, astronomical loss of life and property damage, estimated to be as much as $50 billion over a 200,000 square mile area, would likely result.

Traditionally, the structural engineer has been regarded as the professional with primary responsibility for the seismic performance of a building. This is no longer true, and architects are now seen as having a critical and expanding role to play in mitigating earthquake damage. Architectural decisions concerning site planning, building form and configuration, structural and mechanical system layouts, construction details, and nonstructural components are crucial determinants of the overall performance of a building during an earthquake.

To provide architects with the information they need to make these critical decisions, the AIA/ACSA Research Council has, over the last five years, conducted a series of workshops, funded by the Federal Emergency Management Agency, on the fundamentals of good seismic design. *Buildings at Risk: Seismic Design Basics for Practicing Architects* has evolved directly from the information presented in these workshops, supplemented by research conducted under a grant from the National Science Foundation. The publication is intended to provide practitioners with a solid introduction to basic seismic design principles.

Buildings at Risk is organized into eight key chapters:

- **The Nature of Ground Motion and its Effects on Buildings** provides an overview of how earthquakes impact buildings and how structures react to seismic forces.
- **Site Issues** reviews the potential impact of site conditions on seismic vulnerability.
- **Building Configuration: The Architecture of Seismic Design** examines the best and worst building forms and layouts, concentrating on how to "design in" seismic resistance.
- **Seismically Resistant Structural Systems** covers basic engineering concepts and what architects need to know to work effectively with structural engineers.
- **Basics of Seismic Codes** discusses recent advances in seismic design codes and specifically addresses FEMA's National Earthquake Hazards Reduction Program Provisions.
- **Nonstructural Damage** deals with the "hidden" risk in buildings and how architects, who often have primary responsibility for nonstructural components, can improve performance and avoid costly damage and repair.
- **Seismic Rehabilitation of Existing Buildings** provides a brief introduction to incorporating good seismic design into the growing field of remodeling/retrofitting existing structures.
- **Seismic Design Process** takes a look at how architects and engineers can better interact to produce seismically safer buildings, and
- **The Planning Process** reviews key land use and urban planning concepts to decrease seismic vulnerability.

Buildings at Risk is intended as a comprehensive primer on seismic design, providing basic information that any architect practicing in earthquake country needs to know. The book is not intended as an exhaustive treatment of the subject, and for this reason the publication ends with a glossary of key terms and a list of selected references. The reader is encouraged to access any and all of these references for more in-depth discussions of the topics covered in *Buildings at Risk.*

Chapter 1: The Nature of Ground Motion and its Effect on Buildings

GEOLOGIC BACKGROUND

According to the now generally accepted theory of Plate Tectonics, the earth's crust is divided into several major plates, some 50 miles (80km) thick, that move slowly and continuously over the interior of the earth.

Earthquakes are initiated when, due to slowly accumulating pressure, the ground slips abruptly along a geological fault plane on or near a plate boundary. The resulting waves of vibration within the earth create ground motion at the surface which begins to vibrate in a very complex manner. This, in turn, induces forces within buildings that are determined by the precise nature of the ground motion and the construction characteristics of the building.

The point where the fault first slips is termed the "focus" or "hypocenter." A theoretical point on the earth's surface directly above the focus is termed the "epicenter." (Figure 1.1) The epicenter for the January 17, 1994 Los Angeles earthquake was located in the city of Northridge in the San Fernando Valley.

The initial break in the fault moves rapidly along the line of the fault, and the distance of this movement largely determines the intensity of ground shaking. Thus the 1906 San Francisco earthquake ruptured along some 250 miles (400km) of the San Andreas fault. The Loma Prieta, California earthquake of 1989 was unusual since no surface faulting occured, although a broad area of ground cracking indicated a wide distribution of strain. The fault rupture moved upward to within about 6km of the ground surface area and then spread approximately 20km along the fault to each side of the initial rupture. (Figure 1.2)

GROUND FAILURE

Surface Faulting

Slippage along a fault line deep in the earth's surface may eventually result in *surface faulting*, the crack or split on the earth's surface that provides the layperson's vision of earthquakes. Surface faulting may result in large earth movements: in the 1992 Landers earthquake east of Los Angeles, the earth offset as much as 18 feet at the surface. A building located across a surface fault, no matter how well designed, is almost certain to suffer very severe damage. (Figure 1.3) However, the large disturbance of the ground near a fault is generally quite narrow in width on either side of the fault: in Landers the maximum width of severely disturbed ground was only about 40 meters. Moreover, the probability that buildings will straddle a surface fault is very low

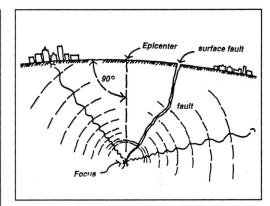

Figure 1.1: Earthquake location

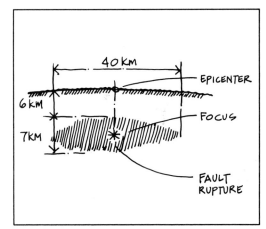

Figure 1.2: The Loma Prieta fault rupture, 1989

Figure 1.3: School straddling a landslide-induced rupture, Alaska

Figure 1.4: House on Turnagain slide

Figure 1.5: Turnagain Heights, Alaska

compared to the likelihood of significant ground motion. So, in seismic design, we design against the vibrations caused by fault slippage and try to ensure that buildings are not built over fault zones.

Landslides, Liquefaction and Subsidence

The energy released by an earthquake can also trigger ground failure in the form of landslides, liquefaction and subsidence which can have devastating effects on a structure. Even well-built structures, designed to withstand earthquake forces, if built on an unstable site or in the path of a landslide, can fall victim.

The Alaskan earthquake of 1964 provides examples of structures with the inherent strength to withstand ground shaking that were devastated as a result of the instability of the sites they were built on. (Figure 1.4) While an architect and contractor could take pride in the performance of their buildings on Turnagain Heights or on 4th Street in Anchorage, the decision to build on geologically unstable sites produced catastrophic results. (Figure 1.5) Avoidance of sites with a potential for liquefaction, landslides or subsidence represents the best design approach.

Ground shaking can also trigger subsidence and liquefaction in soils that are unconsolidated and/or saturated with water. When sandy, water saturated soils are shaken, the bearing capacity of the soil is reduced as the soil liquefies and flows laterally and vertically. Liquefied soils can produce volcano-like sandboils at the ground surface or flow laterally if the soil is not contained. The ground surface and structures built on shallow foundations can subside several feet or be torn apart as spreading occurs. Dramatic examples of liquefaction from recent earthquakes illustrate again, that even well built structures are vulnerable if adequate attention is not paid to site conditions and foundation design. (Figures 1.6 and 1.7)

Figure 1.6: Liquefaction, Niigata, Japan, 1964

GROUND MOTION

While ground failure can be an important consequence of any earthquake, the primary effect buildings are designed to resist is ground motion. During an earthquake, wave vibrations emanate from the line of fault rupture and so approach the building from a given direction. The waves begin like ripples in a still pond when a pebble is thrown into it, but the seismic waves rapidly become more complex.

There are four main wave types, of which "body" waves, within the earth, are the most important for design purposes. (Figure 1.8) First to arrive at the surface is the *P* or *primary* wave. In this wave the ground is successively pushed and pulled along the wave front. The effect is of a sharp punch - it feels as if a truck has hit the building. The P wave is followed by the *S, secondary* or *shear* wave, which is a lateral motion, back and forth (but sideways to the wave front).

The nature of the waves and their interactions are such that actual movement at the ground will be random: predominantly horizontal, often with considerable directional emphasis, but sometimes with a considerable vertical component. The actual horizontal ground displacement is small, only inches even in a large earthquake, except in the immediate area of the fault rupture where displacements of several feet may occur.

THE MEASUREMENT OF GROUND MOTION

Measurement of ground motion is important for design purposes because it provides the basis for determining forces, and assessing the relative seismic hazard at different locations.

Earthquake motion is recorded by a seismograph, an instrument that records the movement, over time, of a freely supported pendulum within a frame: the instrument may be placed on the ground or within a structure.

In modern seismographs, pendulum movement is converted into electronic signals on tape. Strong-motion seismographs, called accelerometers, are designed to directly record nearby rather than distant ground movement, and they produce a record called an accelerogram. Instruments are normally placed so as to measure movements along the two horizontal axes as well as one vertical. Three measures are of major interest: acceleration, velocity, and displacement.

Acceleration, Velocity, Displacement

Acceleration is the rate of change of velocity: when multiplied by mass it results in the inertial force that the building must resist. This is a key measure, and forms the basis of the estimation of earthquake forces on buildings: *Newton's Second Law of Motion* states in essence, that an *inertial force, F, equals mass (M) multiplied by the acceleration (A).*

Figure 1.7: Sand boil in a lettuce field, Watsonville, 1989

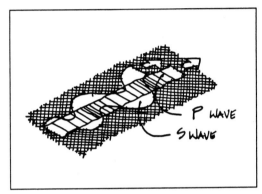

Figure 1.8: "P" and "S" waves

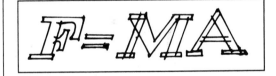

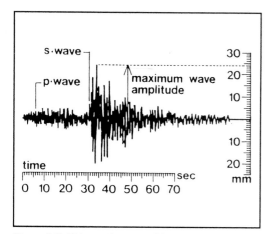

Figure 1.9: This accelerogram illustrates the size of the seismic waves and can be used to derive acceleration, velocity and displacement.

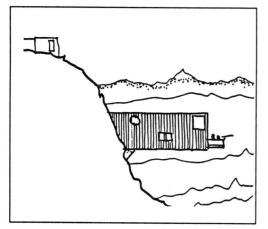

Figure 1.10: A 1.0g design

Acceleration is commonly measured in *"g's"* - the acceleration of a free falling body due to the earth's gravity (approx. 32ft/sec/sec., or 980 cm/sec/sec, or 1.0g.). *Velocity,* measured in inches or centimeters per second, refers to the rate of ground motion at any time. *Displacement,* measured in inches or centimeters, refers to the distance a particle is removed from its "at rest" position. (Figure 1.9)

The level of acceleration generally taken as sufficient to produce some damage to weak construction is 0.10g. The lower limit of acceleration perceptible to people is set by observation and experiment at approximately 0.001g or 1cm/sec^2; at around 0.20g and above most people will have difficulty keeping their footing and sickness symptoms may be induced. An earthquake causing acceleration approaching 0.5g on the ground is very high. On upper floors of buildings, maximum accelerations will often be higher, depending on the degree to which the mass and form of the building act to damp the vibratory effects. A figure of 1.00g, or 100% of gravity, may be reached, for a fraction of a second. To design for 1.00g is diagrammatically equivalent, in a static sense, to designing a building that projects horizontally from a vertical surface. (Figure 1.10) When the behavior of real buildings is observed, several factors modify this diagrammatic equivalence, and structures that could never cantilever from a vertical surface can briefly withstand 1.0g earthquake shaking.

Acceleration is the measure commonly used to indicate the possible destructive power of an earthquake in relation to a building. A more significant measure is that of acceleration combined with *duration*, which takes into account the impact of earthquake forces over time. In general, a number of cycles of moderate acceleration, sustained over time, can be much more difficult for a building to withstand than a single peak of much higher value. Seismic instrumentation also measures the duration of strong ground motion, which generally relates to the length of the fault break.

Typically the extreme vibration will occupy only a few seconds; both the 1989 Loma Prieta and 1994 Northridge earthquakes lasted only a little over ten seconds, yet they caused much destruction. In 1906, in San Francisco, the severe shaking lasted about 45 seconds; in Alaska in 1964 the severe earthquake motion lasted for over 3 minutes.

Two earthquake measurement systems are in common use and neither, for various reasons, is really satisfactory from the building design viewpoint.

Magnitude: The Size of the Wave

Earthquake *magnitude* is the first measure: it is expressed as Richter magnitude based on the scale devised by Professor Charles Richter of the California Institute of Technology in 1935. Richter's scale is based on the *maximum* amplitude of certain seismic waves recorded on a standard seismograph at a distance of 100 kilometers from the earthquake epicenter. The scale, however, tells nothing about duration, which may be of great significance in causing damage, nor does it tell anything about frequency content which, in its relationship to the building period, as discussed later, is also of great significance in determining damage. Because the instrument is unlikely to be exactly 100km from the source, Richter developed a method to allow for the diminishing of wave amplitude (or *"attenuation"*) with increased distance, just as the light of a star appears dimmer with distance. (Figure 1.11)

Because the size of earthquakes varies enormously, the graphic range of wave amplitude measured on seismographs is compressed by using, as a scale, the *logarithm to base ten* of the recorded wave amplitude. Hence, each unit of Richter magnitude indicates a *10* times increase in wave amplitude. But the *energy increase* represented by each unit of scale is estimated by seismologists as approximately *31* times. Since Richter magnitude is a measured quantity, the scale is open-ended, but seismologists believe that a Richter magnitude of about 9 represents the largest possible earthquake. A given earthquake will have only one Richter magnitude, though differences in recording result in some argument as to what this will be.*

Intensity: The Amount of Damage

To provide information directly related to local shaking and building damage, *intensity* scales are used. These scales are based on subjective observation of the effects of the earthquake on buildings, ground and people. In the United States the most commonly used scale is the *Modified Mercalli (MM)* originally developed in Europe in 1902, and modified in 1931 to fit construction conditions then prevalent in California and other parts of the United States.

As a result the MM scale is somewhat dated, with no references to common modern construction systems. This is not much of a disadvantage because earthquake damage is most likely to be concentrated in older buildings, often of the very type that the scale describes. (Figure 1.12) The MM Scale is a twelve point scale, *I - XII*. The descriptions for MM I are, in abbreviated form, "Not felt. Marginal and long-period effects of large earthquakes." For MM XII the descriptor reads, "Damage nearly total. Large rock masses displaced. Lines of sight and level distorted. Objects thrown into the air." Because earthquake effects vary depending on distance from the epicenter, nature of the ground, and magnitude, an earthquake will have many MM values. The MM scale has been correlated with ground acceleration. For example, MM VII corresponds to a peak acceleration between approximately 0.1g and 0.29g.

THE EFFECTS OF GROUND MOTION

Inertial Forces

While the effects of ground failure can be extremely severe, the most common and widespread cause of earthquake damage is ground shaking. Seismically induced shaking affects buildings in three primary ways: inertial forces, period and resonance, and torsion. Shaking causes damage by internally generated inertial forces generated by vibration of the building's mass.

* The use of the term Richter Magnitude will eventually be replaced by the use of the terms 'preliminary magnitude' and 'moment magnitude.'

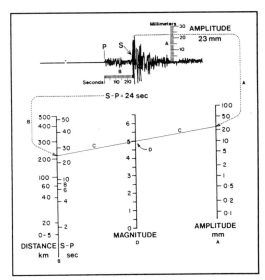

Figure 1.11: Richter magnitude

Figure 1.12: Damage to an older masonry building

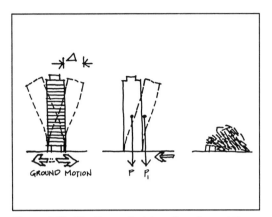

Figure 1.13: The P-e or P-delta effect. Lateral forces cause structure to drift (Δ). This displaces the vertical loads from P to P_1: extreme displacement causes collapse.

As noted above, inertial forces are the product of mass and acceleration (Newton's $F = MxA$). Acceleration is the change of velocity (or speed in a certain direction) over time and is a function of the nature of the earthquake; mass is an attribute of the building and, at ground level, is equivalent to the building weight. (On the moon, building mass and weight would be quite different.) Since the forces are inertial, an increase in mass will result in an increase in the force for a given acceleration. Hence, there is an immediate advantage when lightweight construction is used as a seismic design approach.

Another detrimental aspect of mass, besides its role in increasing the lateral loads, is that failure of vertical elements such as columns and walls can occur by buckling, when the mass pushing down due to gravity exerts its force on a member bent or moved out of plumb by the lateral forces. This phenomenon is known as the *P-e*, or *P-delta* effect. (Figure 1.13)

Period and Amplification

Another important characteristic of earthquake waves is their period (the inverse of frequency), for example: Are the waves quick and abrupt, or slow and rolling? This information is particularly important for the determination of seismic forces.

All objects have a natural, or fundamental, period. This is the rate at which they will vibrate if they are given a horizontal push. In fact, without dragging it back and forth, it is not possible to make an object vibrate at anything other than its natural period. When a child on a swing is started with a push, to be effective this shove must be as close as possible to the natural period of the swing. If correctly gauged, a very small push will set the swing going effectively. Similarly, when the earthquake ground motion starts a building vibrating it will tend to sway back and forth at its natural period.

When a vibrating structure is given further pushes that are also at its natural period the structure tends to *resonate*. Its vibrations increase dramatically for

Figure 1.14: Fundamental periods

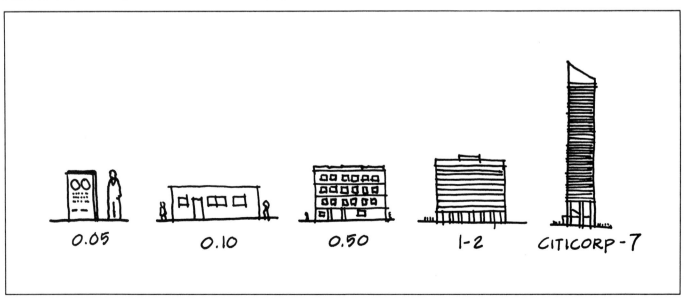

rather small pushes and, in fact, its accelerations may increase as much as four or five times.

The natural periods of structures vary from about *0.05 seconds* for a piece of equipment such as a filing cabinet to about *0.10 seconds* for a one story building. A four story building will sway at about a *0.50 second* period, and taller buildings between 10 and 20 stories will swing at periods of about *1 to 2 seconds*. An approximate rule of thumb is that the building period equals the *number of stories divided by ten*. Period is primarily a function of height. The sixty story Citicorp building in New York has a measured period of *7 seconds* - give it a push and it will sway slowly back and forth, completing a cycle every 7 seconds. (Figure 1.14)

Other factors, such as the stiffness of the building's construction materials and the building's geometric proportions, also affect the period, but height is the most important consideration. In addition, taller buildings undergo several *modes of vibration*, so the buildings sway back and forth in a very complex manner. (Figure 1.15) For seismic purposes the natural period is generally the most significant.

The ground also vibrates at its natural period: the natural period of ground in the United States generally varies from about *0.4 seconds* to *1.5 seconds*, depending primarily on the hardness of the ground. Very soft ground may have a period of up to *2 seconds*. The ground cannot sustain longer periods except under certain unusual conditions.

Clearly, this range is well within that of common building periods, so it is quite possible that the motion the ground transmits to the building will be at its natural period. This may create resonance and the structure may have to deal with accelerations of perhaps *1.0g* when the ground is only vibrating with accelerations of *0.2g*.

Amplification in building vibration is very undesirable. The possibility of this happening can be reduced by trying to ensure that the building period will not coincide with the ground. The design of a short stiff (short period) building, if located on soft (long period) ground, would be appropriate. This is acceptable for new buildings but, there are many inappropriate buildings which were designed before this phenomena was fully understood. The terrible destruction in the 1985 Mexico City earthquake was primarily the result of response amplification caused by coincidence of the building and ground motion periods. (Figure 1.16)

There is also a more general effect related to different types of ground. Earthquake shaking tends to be greater on soft ground than on hard ground - such as rock. As a result, earthquake damage tends to be more severe in areas of soft ground. This characteristic became very clear when the 1906 San Francisco earthquake was studied, and maps were drawn which showed building damage in relation to known ground geology. Studies after the 1989 Loma Prieta earthquake showed that shaking in the soft ground around San Francisco bay was *2 1/2* to *3 1/2* times that of shaking in rock.

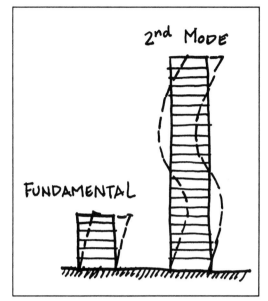

Figure 1.15: Modes of vibration

Figure 1.16: Total collapse caused by extreme response, Mexico City.

National Institute of Standards and Technology

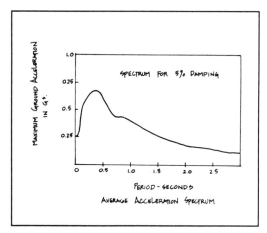

Figure 1.17: Sample response spectrum

Figure 1.18: Furniture upset by motion in a high-rise building.

If the period of a new building is close to that of the site, curves can be drawn for the site, based on information about the nature of the ground, that estimate the periods at which *maximum building response* is likely. That is, the building periods for which maximum shaking can be anticipated. Such a curve is called the site *response spectrum.* (Figure 1.17) Each site will have its own distinctive response spectrum.

The response spectrum generally shows the accelerations (on the vertical ordinate) that may be expected at varying periods (the horizontal ordinate). Thus the response spectrum illustrated here shows a maximum response at a period of about 0.5 seconds - a mid-rise building. Based on this knowledge the building design might be adjusted to ensure that the building period will not coincide with the site period of maximum response. For the figure shown, with a maximum response at about 0.5 seconds, it would be appropriate to design a building with a longer period, of 1 second or more. Of course, it is not always possible to do this, but the response spectrum shows clearly what the possible accelerations at different periods are likely to be, and the building can be designed accordingly.

Response spectra are commonly of the form shown -- that is, the maximum response is at the short period end, and then the response tails off, reducing significantly as longer periods are reached. Currently our codes recognize the beneficial aspect of flexibility (long period) by permitting lower design coefficients. However, the amount of motion experienced by these structures means that they may suffer considerable damage to their nonstructural components such as ceilings and partitions, and contents such as filing cabinets and bookshelves, in even a modest earthquake. (Figure 1.18)

The design technique of base isolation, discussed in Chapter 4, is based on *shifting* the building period towards the long period of the spectrum where the response is reduced. Most base isolation systems shift the building period into the 2 second range. Of course, if the building was located on a site with a period of 2 seconds, base isolation would not be effective and would, indeed, probably lead to serious resonance.

It is generally true that locations closer to the fault from where the energy is released will experience higher frequency (i.e. shorter period) ground motion, and at large distances the motions will probably be of lower frequency, the type which eye-witnesses describe as rolling, slowly rocking, swaying, etc. Thus the distance of a building from a fault also affects the kind of ground motion that may be encountered. High-rise buildings located a long distance (over one hundred miles) from the earthquake focus may be subjected to considerable long-period motion. In Mexico City, the earthquake focus was two hundred and fifty miles from the area of highest damage. (Figure 1.19)

Torsion

The center of mass, or center of gravity, of an object is the point at which it could be exactly balanced without any rotation resulting. A uniformly distributed mass results in the coincidence of a plan's geometric center with the center of mass. An eccentric distribution of mass locates its center away from the geometric center.

If the mass within a floor is uniformly distributed, then the resultant force of the *horizontal* acceleration of all its particles of mass is exerted through the floor's center. If the resultant of the resistance (provided by walls or frames) pushes back through this point, dynamic balance is maintained.

If the mass is eccentrically disposed with respect to the center of resistance, the earthquake force will be eccentric as well, since the earthquake only generates forces because of the presence of mass, and the amount of force is directly proportional to the amount of mass. In this instance the floor will tend to rotate about the center of resistance, thus creating "*torsion*" - a twisting action in plan, which results in a very undesirable kind of stress concentration. (Figure 1.20)

In a building in which the mass is approximately evenly distributed in plan (typical of a symmetrical building with uniform floor, wall and column masses), ideally the earthquake resistant elements would be symmetrically placed in all directions, so no matter which direction the floors are pushed, the structure pushes back with a balanced stiffness that prevents rotation from occuring.

In practice, some degree of torsion is always present, and the building code makes provision for this.

RESISTING THE EFFECTS OF GROUND MOTION

Three basic characteristics of buildings help resist and dissipate the effects of seismically-induced motion: damping, ductility and strength/stiffness.

Damping

Damping affects the dynamic behavior of the building and modifies its response to ground motion. If a building resonates with the efficiency of a swing or a pendulum in response to ground motion, its acceleration will greatly amplify and seismic forces will significantly increase.

However, buildings are prevented from resonating with the purity of a pendulum because they are damped: that is, they are rather inefficient in their vibration and when set in motion tend to return to their starting position quickly. The extent of damping in a building depends on its connections, nonstructural elements and construction materials, and design assumptions are commonly made about the extent of damping based on knowledge of previous structures.

When damping is introduced, the general response remains the same, but the magnitude is greatly reduced. Although damping is theoretically subject to alteration (through changes in the live load, for example), in practice it is not generally regarded as a design variable.

Figure 1.19: Damage caused by long period motion, Mexico City.

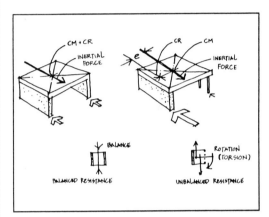

Figure 1.20: Torsion: balanced and unbalanced resistance

Figure 1.21: Ductile materials undergo considerable permanent deformation before failure.

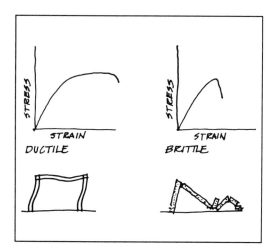

Figure 1.22: Brittle failure caused by lack of ductility in the structural system.

Ductility

Even if resonance is avoided, and the building is well damped, a building in a severe earthquake may still be subject to forces that are much higher than those provided for in the building codes. To design for maximum forces would result in a very uneconomic design, and the size and placement of resisting elements would pose planning and architectural problems.

The gap between design capacity (the computed ability of a building to withstand calculated forces) and possible actual forces is largely dealt with by relying on the material property of "ductility". This is the property of certain materials - steel in particular - to fail only after considerable inelastic (i.e. permanent) deformation has taken place. This deformation, or distortion, dissipates the energy of the earthquake. (Figure 1.21) To achieve good ductility also requires special, and sometimes expensive, detailing of joints.

Brittle materials, such as unreinforced masonry, or inadequately reinforced concrete, fail suddenly, with a minimum of prior distortion: they have inadequate ductility. (Figure 1.22)

There are, however, many instances when buildings have encountered much more than the forces for which they were designed and yet have survived, sometimes with little damage. This can be explained by the fact that the analysis of forces is not precise and deliberately errs on the conservative side, so that the building can really survive higher forces than is apparent. In addition, the building often gains additional strength from components, such as partitions, that are not considered in the analysis. Finally, materials are often stronger than the engineer assumes in his calculations: all these factors add up to a considerable safety factor, or uncalculated additional resistance.

Strength and Stiffness

Strength and stiffness are two of the most important characteristics of any structure. Although these two concepts are present in non-seismic structural design and analysis, the distinction between strength and stiffness is perhaps most critical, and its study most highly developed, in structural engineering as applied to the earthquake problem.

A familiar measure of stiffness in the vertical sense is *deflection*; in the sizing of floor joists, for example, deflection rather than strength often governs because a "bouncy" floor is undesirable, though perfectly safe. The analogous lateral force condition is when limitations on *drift*, the horizontal story-to-story deflection, impose more severe requirements on members than the strength requirements. (Figure 1.23)

The strength problem is that of resisting a given load without exceeding a safe stress in the material: the stiffness or horizontal deflection problem is that of preventing the structure from moving out of vertical alignment more than a given amount. In the design of a floor system, the joists may tolerate a certain deflection but the ceiling finish cannot. Similarly, drift must be limited, even if the structure can tolerate more, because of its effect on nonstructural components - particularly partition, cladding and ceiling elements - and its effect on the comfort of occupants.

The *relative* rigidities of members are a major concern in seismic analysis. As soon as a rigid horizontal element, or diaphragm, such as a concrete slab, is tied to vertical resisting elements, it will force those elements to deflect the same amount. If two elements (two frames, walls, braces, or any combination) are forced to deflect the same amount, and if one is stiffer, that one will take more of the load. Why this is so can be visualized from the diagram which shows a heavy block supported away from a wall by two short beams: clearly, the thick stiff beam will carry much more load than the slender one, and the same is true if they are turned 90 degrees to simulate the lateral force situation. (Figure 1.24)

Mathematically, the stiffness of a column varies approximately as the inverse of the cube of the length. In this diagram the columns have the same cross section but the short column is half the length of the long one. Therefore, the short column will be *eight* times stiffer (2^3) instead of *twice* as stiff, and will take *eight times the load* of the long column. This has serious implications for buildings with columns of different lengths. (Figure 1.25)

Only if the member stiffnesses are identical can it be assumed that they share the load equally. Since concrete slab floors or roofs will generally fit into the "rigid diaphragm" classification, and since it is unusual for all walls, frames, or braced frames to be identical, the evaluation of relative rigidities is a necessary part of most seismic analysis problems to determine the relative distribution of the total horizontal force to the various resisting elements.

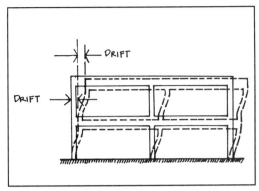

Figure 1.23: Story-to-story drift

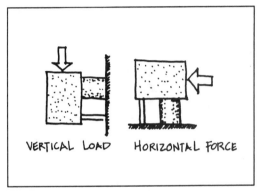

Figure 1.24: Whether a beam or a column, the thick supporting member will carry much more load.

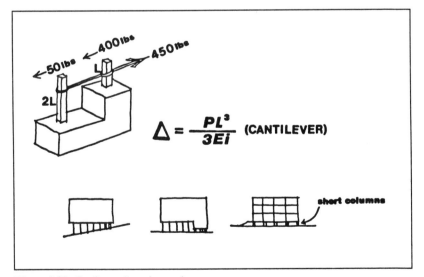

$$\Delta = \frac{PL^3}{3Ei} \text{ (CANTILEVER)}$$

Figure 1.25: Configuration, short columns

Chapter 2: Site Issues

SITING OF A STRUCTURE - WHERE DOES THE SITE BEGIN?

From a seismic design standpoint, the "site" is the region within which a structure will be built; and while it is critical that a structure not be built across an active fault trace, it is equally important that siting and design decisions address the potential for increased intensity and duration of ground shaking, accessibility, survival of life lines and potentially hazardous adjacent land uses. Thus, seismic design is not limited to an analysis of the factors within the confines of the site boundary; it extends to a broad environmental analysis of regional and community vulnerability.

SEISMIC RISK AS A SITING CRITERIA

The factors that impact site vulnerability include proximity to active earthquake faults; susceptibility of the site to ground shaking; the potential for ground failure, including subsidence, lateral spreading, liquefaction, and landslides; adjacent structures and land uses that could pose a threat during or after an earthquakes; and, the potential for inundation resulting from tsunami or dam failure.

From a site and urban planning standpoint, however, concern should not be limited to the identification on the site of a fault or potential fault rupture, but to the broader impact of ground shaking and geologic failures that could occur in the region. The failure of the regional transportation network, disruption of power or water supply or the isolation of building as a result of ground failure, can be as devastating to a business as actual structural damage.

Therefore, seismic risks from beyond the building site property line must be considered as design criteria for a structure. These criteria address the relative desirability or risk of an individual site, that is, is one site safer for a particular use than another site; and what factors beyond the site boundary, such as adjacent land uses, geologic stability of adjacent land, or the survivability of lifelines or access, could impact site development?

ACTIVE EARTHQUAKE FAULTS

If a structure is built over an active fault trace, it should be designed to accommodate displacement or fault offset. (Figure 2.1)

This is both a challenging and costly effort, with no guarantee of success. The mapping of active faults has been a focus of geologists and urban planners for

Figure 2.1: San Andreas fault in Central California

Richard Eisner

Figure 2.2: The section of Fairmont Hospital in San Leandro, California, built across a fault trace, was removed.

several decades. It has been a critical element increasing our understanding of regional seismicity: the frequency of seismic activity, the magnitude of previous seismic events, and the potential for future seismic activity. The fault maps indicate where active surface faulting is identified and where future offset potential exists. Where identified, designers should provide a setback from identified faults for new construction.

In many areas, development is limited or prohibited within defined zones adjacent to active faults. Programs to map fault zones and limit new construction within established zones have proven successful in reducing earthquake risks to new construction. Unfortunately, earthquake fault traces were often ignored when land was subdivided and developed, presenting a costly dilemma to owners of existing structures in a fault zone.

Where existing structures are built across fault lines, their structural performance, occupancy and continued use should be reviewed to evaluate the risk they pose. Those sections of structures built across a trace can be removed or occupancy types and loads can be reduced to reduce risk exposure. (Figure 2.2)

IMPACT OF REGIONAL GEOLOGY ON SITE PERFORMANCE

The geology of a region plays a significant role in determining the potential for shaking and ground failure damage. In relatively old geological regions, such as the eastern and midwestern United States where weathering and erosion have leveled the terrain and laid deep deposits of unconsolidated soils, violent ground shaking resulting from fault rupture thousands of feet below the earth's surface can extend for thousands of square miles. Deep soils can amplify ground shaking intensity, extend duration of violent shaking and limit attenuation of shaking; resulting in greater damage over a larger area than would result in younger or bedrock regions.

For example, in the central United States, the violent shaking of the New Madrid, Missouri earthquakes of 1811 and 1812 extended across the midwest and was felt as far away as the eastern seaboard. The earthquakes were felt over 2,000,000 square miles! In contrast, the 1906 San Francisco earthquake, estimated to have released 30 times more energy, was felt over only 375,000 square miles. It impacted a much smaller area because the regional geology in California limited propagation and increased attenuation of shaking. In both examples, one without surface manifestations of faulting, and the other with visible surface faulting, regional geology rather than presence of a surface fault determined the extent of potential damage. (Figure 2.3)

While not building across an earthquake fault is certainly a good rule, building adjacent to a fault may not pose as great a risk as one would expect. A number of recent earthquakes have emphasized that regional and local geology and the lack of attenuation of ground shaking are often more important than proximity to the earthquake's epicenter in determining the impact of an earthquake. The 1985 Mexican earthquake occurred on the coast of Mexico between Acapulco and Ixtapa. Damage close to the epicenter in the coastal resort areas was minor.

However, 250 miles away in Mexico City, the damage to midrise concrete structures was severe, resulting in several thousand deaths. Again in 1989, the Loma Prieta earthquake, centered in the Santa Cruz Mountains resulted in the deaths of more than 40 persons on the Cypress Viaduct, 60 miles north of Santa Cruz in Oakland. In both cases, the most violent ground shaking did not occur at the epicenter of the earthquakes, but a significant distance away as a result of the propagation of the ground waves, the geology of the region and local soil conditions. Understanding the regional and local geology can tell the designer a great deal about the relative risk of an individual site.

REGIONAL DAMAGE AND ITS IMPACT ON A SITE

Continued function and operation of a building depends on more than merely the performance of the structure. Damage to lifeline systems providing water, sewer, power, transportation and communication services can isolate a structure, cease operations or production, and leave the structure vulnerable to secondary hazards of fire and hazardous material releases. For buildings containing functions where power, water and/or communications is vital for continued operations or safety, analysis should address the vulnerability of regional lifelines serving the site. If access to the site or to regional transportation networks is critical for ongoing operations or for reaching and maintaining market deliveries, the designer should review the vulnerability of the regional transportation system. (Figure 2.4) While these issues cannot be addressed in building design, their identification for the clients will provide a basis for their understanding of the strengths and limits of a specific site, and for determining the need for back-up facilities, water and power sources, and communication systems that may prove critical to safety and post-earthquake response, recovery, and continued business operations.

Regional damage, well beyond the property line, can result in isolation of a facility from resources, market or employees, dislocation, and severe economic disruption, even without damage to the structure.

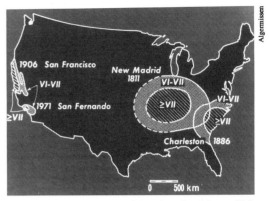

Figure 2.3: Comparison of isoseismals of large U.S. earthquakes

Figure 2.4: Ground failure occurred at this highway, overstressing column/slab connections.

Christopher Arnold

THE ARCHITECT'S ROLE IN SITE SELECTION AND EVALUATION

Only occasionally is the architect responsible for site selection. Most often, the architect is provided with a site by a client unaware of its vulnerability to seismic forces. The more traditional site analysis would include relevant information on zoning and planning restrictions on the site. A "seismic site analysis" should include an evaluation of local site conditions, adjacent hazards and regional geology, to assist the architect in briefing the client on the expected performance of the selected site, the survivability of transportation and access to the site, and the vulnerability of lifelines serving the site. This data can provide valuable insights for the client and design team in establishing design parameters and in defining expected seismic performance of the structure.

If, however, the architect participates in site selection, desired structural building performance and post earthquake function can be measured against expected site performance, life line survival and site access in determining the most appropriate location.

In either situation, a site analysis should include an assessment of the environment beyond the property line and include adjacent structures and site conditions that could "spill over" onto your site. (Figure 2.5) A complete analysis should address the issues identified in the Site Analysis Checklist.

Figure 2.5: Building adjacencies can have major impacts on performance during earthquakes. A large number of structures suffered pounding damage during the 1985 Mexico City event, leading in many cases to partial or full collapse.

Christopher Arnold

Site Analysis Checklist

❑ Is there an active fault on or adjacent to the site?

❑ Will the site geology increase ground shaking?
Does the site contain unconsolidated natural or man-made fills?

❑ Is the site geology stable?

❑ Is the site susceptible to liquefaction?

❑ Are adjacent up-slope and down-slope environments stable?

❑ Are post-earthquake access and egress secure?

❑ Are transportation, communication and utility lifelines vulnerable to disruption and failure?

❑ Are there adjacent land uses that could be hazardous after an earthquake?

❑ Are hazardous materials stored or used in the vicinity?

❑ Are building setbacks adequate to prevent battering from adjacent structures?

❑ Are adjacent structures collapse hazards? Would they collapse onto your site or would their failure otherwise impact the functions of your structure?

❑ Is the site subject to inundation from tsunami? Seiche? Dam failure flooding?

❑ Are there areas of the site that should be left undeveloped due to:
· Landslide potential?
· Inundation potential?
· High potential for liquefaction?
· Expected surface faulting?
· More violent or longer duration ground shaking expected?
· Areas necessary to provide separation from adjacent uses or structures?

❑ Is there adequate space on the site for a safe and "defensible" area of refuge from hazards for building occupants?

❑ Does the site plan increase potential for earthquake-induced landslides by:
· Cutting unstable slopes?
· Increasing surface runoff?
· Increasing soil water content?

Chapter 3: Building Configuration: The Architecture of Seismic Design

BUILDING CONFIGURATION EFFECTS

Experience in earthquakes has shown that the architectural form of a building has a major influence on its performance under ground motion. This influence is the result of the three dimensional interaction of all the structural systems and architectural components under earthquake forces. For certain architectural forms, the *response of the building* can become very complex, and the earthquake forces can be concentrated and distributed in undesirable ways.

The term *building configuration* is used in seismic design to define the architectural form of a building. Architectural features of concern are defined in the following sections.

CONFIGURATION DEFINED

The kinds of unusual conditions and buildings that are of concern result from early architectural decisions that determine the *configuration* of the building. For these purposes, configuration can be defined as: *building size and shape, the size and location of structural elements, and the nature, size and location of nonstructural elements that may affect structural performance.* (Figure 3.1) The latter includes such elements as heavy nonstructural walls, staircases, exterior wall panels and heavy equipment items.

The seismic significance of the building configuration is that it primarily determines both the way forces are *distributed* throughout the structure and also the *relative magnitude* of those forces. Seismic codes distinguish between *regular* and *irregular* configurations, and it is the latter that may have a detrimental influence on the effectiveness and cost of seismic engineering and on building seismic performance itself. Code forces, discussed in Chapter 5, are based on the assumption of a regular configuration. (Figure 3.2)

Figure 3.2: The impact of building configuration on seismic performance has only begun to be recognized in building codes. A wide range of existing buildings have been designed without taking such considerations into account, such as this soft first story example in San Francisco.

Figure 3.1: Configuration components

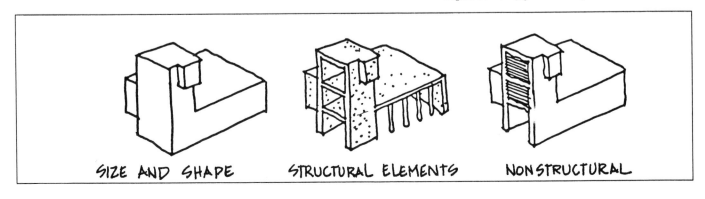

SIZE AND SHAPE STRUCTURAL ELEMENTS NONSTRUCTURAL

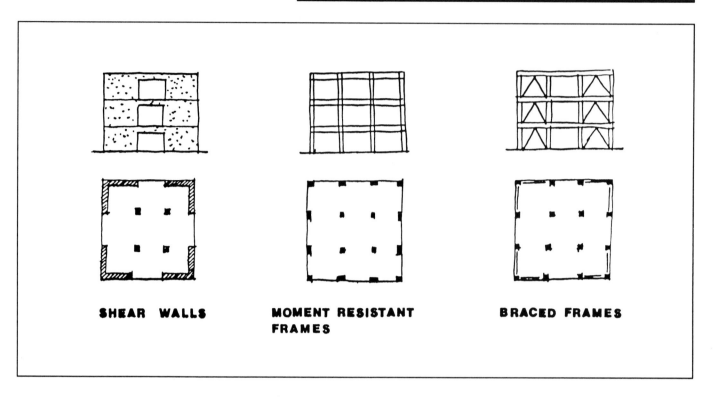

Figure 3.3: Regular (uniform) configurations

REGULAR CONFIGURATIONS

The kind of regular (or uniform) configuration upon which the estimate of code seismic forces is based is shown in Figure 3.3. These three diagrams represent structures that are seismically optimal, which use the three main alternatives for lateral resistance systems, and which still provide a useful and common architectural form. The characteristics of these configurations that make them optimal, or desirable, are shown in **Table 3.A**. (The particular structure shown, a three story, three bay building, is one example. Other building heights, and number of uniform bays would be equally satisfactory, unless the building had undesirable attributes of size or proportion as discussed below.)

Low Height to Base Ratio

Equal Floor Heights

Symmetrical Plan

Uniform Section and Elevations

Maximum Torsional Resistance

Balanced Resistance

Short Spans/Redundancy

Direct Load Paths

Table 3.A: *Optimal seismic design*

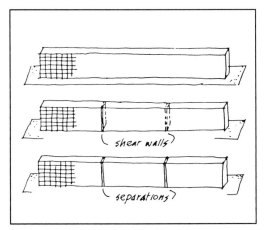

Figure 3.4: Building size will affect seismic response. Buildings that are large in plan may have difficulty responding as one unit to seismic forces.

Buildings of circular plan form are, in theory, even better configurations because of their total symmetry, but they are structurally more complex and, in general, not very useful in planning and urban design terms.

Not all regular building forms, however, are equally effective as seismic configurations. The size and geometrical proportions of a building also affect its seismic response.

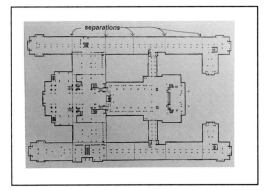

Figure 3.5: Plan, Imperial Hotel

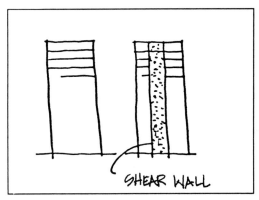

Figure 3.6: Problems of proportion apply to resistive elements such as shear walls.

Buildings that are very large in plan (such as some industrial or warehouse type buildings) may have difficulty in responding as one unit to seismic vibration. This may cause additional longitudinal compressive-tensile stresses and horizontal displacements. Different locations in the building may respond out of phase with one another, instead of as a single unit.

Very large forces may build up in the diaphragms that must be resisted by shear walls or frames. The solution is to add shear walls or frames (to reduce the span of the diaphragm), recognizing that this may present internal planning problems. Alternatively, the building may be broken up into smaller units, separated by seismic joints. This is an ideal solution seismically, but introduces difficult architectural detailing problems at the joints between building units. (Figure 3.4)

Similarly, buildings that are extremely long in elevation (though not large in plan) may develop large forces in shear walls or frames, and in the diaphragm. The solution is the same: add cross walls or frames, or subdivide the building. The long wings of Frank Lloyd Wright's Imperial Hotel in Tokyo, for example, were actually divided into a large number of separate small rectangular buildings which, probably much more than the highly publicized foundation system, helped the structure survive the 1923 Tokyo earthquake. (Figure 3.5)

Proportion problems in very slender buildings primarily relate to the possibility of *overturning*. While this may apply to the form of the entire building it more commonly relates to the proportions of resisting elements such as shear walls. (Figure 3.6)

From: U.S. Coast and Geodetic Survey

Figure 3.7: Variations in perimeter resistance can cause torsional failures such as this J.C. Penney store in the 1964 Alaska quake.

IRREGULAR CONFIGURATIONS

Irregular configurations occur when the building deviates from a simple regular, symmetrical form in plan and section. This deviation tends to create two basic kinds of problems:

- Torsion
- Stress concentration

Torsional problems are most typically associated with plan irregularity or geometries, where the size and location of vertical elements produce eccentricity between the centers of mass and resistance. Torsional forces create great uncertainty in analyzing the building's resistance.

Stress concentrations occur when an undue proportion of the overall seismic force is concentrated at one or a few locations in the building, such as a particular set of beams or columns.

Many building failures occur because of the lack of balanced resistance, which results in undue stress being placed on a member or members, with consequent overstress or failure. Torsional forces and stress concentrations induced by configuration irregularities, such as abrupt changes of strength or stiffness, are the prime cause of such imbalances. (Figure 3.7)

Configuration irregularities often arise for sound planning or urban design reasons and are not necessarily the result of the designer's whim (or ignorance). For example, the re-entrant corner forms are very useful in achieving high density housing solutions on small lots. (Figure 3.8) High first stories may be necessary for buildings such as hotels or offices in which large first floor spaces require much higher ceilings than smaller rooms on upper floors. Understanding the seismic effect of configuration irregularity will enable necessary irregularity to be accommodated without significant detriment to seismic performance.

CONFIGURATION IRREGULARITY AND THE CODE

To establish seismic forces for practical design purposes by use of a seismic code, a number of assumptions must be made. Typical of these assumptions are that the forces are analyzed in *two directions*, loads are analyzed independently and aggregated by *simple addition*, and structures are assumed to provide *direct load paths* and be *regular in form* (defined in Chapter 5).

The code procedures commonly in use for establishing earthquake forces apply to structures based on these simplifying assumptions. Until the 1973 edition of the Uniform Building Code the configuration problem was not dealt with in a specific clause at all, and until the 1988 edition of the code the problem was only covered by a general caveat:

"Structures having irregular shapes or framing systems: the distribution of

Figure 3.8: Re-entrant corner shapes

the lateral forces in structures which have highly irregular shapes, large differences in lateral resistance or stiffness between adjacent stories or other unusual features shall be determined *considering the dynamic characteristics of the structure*" (italics added).

So, the designer must use his judgment and knowledge in assessing the magnitude and distribution of the code forces.

The **1975 Commentary** to the *Recommended Lateral Force Requirements*, published by the Structural Engineers Association of California (SEAOC), which provides the technical basis for the *Uniform Building Code*, explained why the problem was dealt with only in a judgmental way:

"These minimum standards have, in general, been written for uniform buildings and conditions. The subsequent application of these minimum standards to unusual buildings or conditions has, in many instances, led to an unrealistic evaluation."

"... Due to the infinite variations of irregularities that can exist, the impracticality of establishing definite parameters and rational rules for the application of this section are readily apparent."

Commentary: Recommended Lateral Force Requirements (1975) SEAOC.

In essence, the seismic design problem has historically been too complex to be dealt with by simple quantitative code rules, and must be left to engineering judgment. However, starting with the 1988 Uniform Building Code and the 1988 NEHRP Provisions, configuration irregularities are defined on a quantitative basis, and a more elaborate *modal analysis* is required where certain irregularities occur. The requirements that trigger modal analysis are complex and, in general, only apply to buildings over 5 stories or 65 feet in height, located in Zones 3 and 4 (UBC). In the UBC and NEHRP Provisions, configuration irregularities are defined in 2 tables, reprinted in Figures 3.9 and 3.10, that refer to vertical and plan structural irregularities.

TABLE NO. 23-M
VERTICAL STRUCTURAL IRREGULARITIES

IRREGULARITY TYPE AND DEFINITION	REFERENCE SECTION
A. **Stiffness Irregularity—Soft Story**	
A soft story is one in which the lateral stiffness is less than 70 percent of that in the story above or less than 80 percent of the average stiffness of the three stories above.	2312 (d) 8 C (ii)
B. **Weight (mass) Irregularity**	
Mass irregularity shall be considered to exist where the effective mass of any story is more than 150 percent of the effective mass of an adjacent story. A roof which is lighter than the floor below need not be considered.	2312 (d) 8 C (ii)
C. **Vertical Geometric Irregularity**	
Vertical geometric irregularity shall be considered to exist where the horizontal dimension of the lateral force-resisting system in any story is more than 130 percent of that in an adjacent story. One-story penthouses need not be considered.	2312 (d) 8 C (ii)
D. **In-plane Discontinuity in Vertical Lateral Force-resisting Element**	
An in-plane offset of the lateral load-resisting elements greater than the length of those elements.	2312 (e) 7
E. **Discontinuity in Capacity—Weak Story**	
A weak story is one in which the story strength is less than 80 percent of that in the story above. The story strength is the total strength of all seismic resisting elements sharing the story shear for the direction under consideration.	2312 (d) 9 A

TABLE NO. 23-N
PLAN STRUCTURAL IRREGULARITIES

IRREGULARITY TYPE AND DEFINITION	REFERENCE SECTION
A. **Torsional Irregularity—to be considered when diaphragms are not flexible.**	
Torsional irregularity shall be considered to exist when the maximum story drift, computed including accidental torsion, at one end of the structure transverse to an axis is more than 1.2 times the average of the story drifts of the two ends of the structure.	2312 (h) 2 1 (v)
B. **Reentrant Corners**	
Plan configurations of a structure and its lateral force-resisting system contain reentrant corners, where both projections of the structure beyond a reentrant corner are greater than 15 percent of the plan dimension of the structure in the given direction.	2312 (h) 2 1 (v) 2312 (h) 2 1 (vi)
C. **Diaphragm Discontinuity**	
Diaphragms with abrupt discontinuities or variations in stiffness, including those having cutout or open areas greater than 50 percent of the gross enclosed area of the diaphragm, or changes in effective diaphragm stiffness of more than 50 percent from one story to the next.	2312 (h) 2 1 (v)
D. **Out-of-plane Offsets**	
Discontinuities in a lateral force path, such as out-of-plane offsets of the vertical elements.	2312 (e) 7, 2312 (h) 2 1 (v)
E. **Nonparallel Systems**	
The vertical lateral load-resisting elements are not parallel to nor symmetric about the major orthogonal axes of the lateral force-resisting system.	2312 (h) 1

Figures 3.9 and Figure 3.10: Irregular Configuration Tables. Reproduced from the 1991 edition of the Uniform Building Code ©1991, with permission from the publishers, the International Conference of Building Officials.

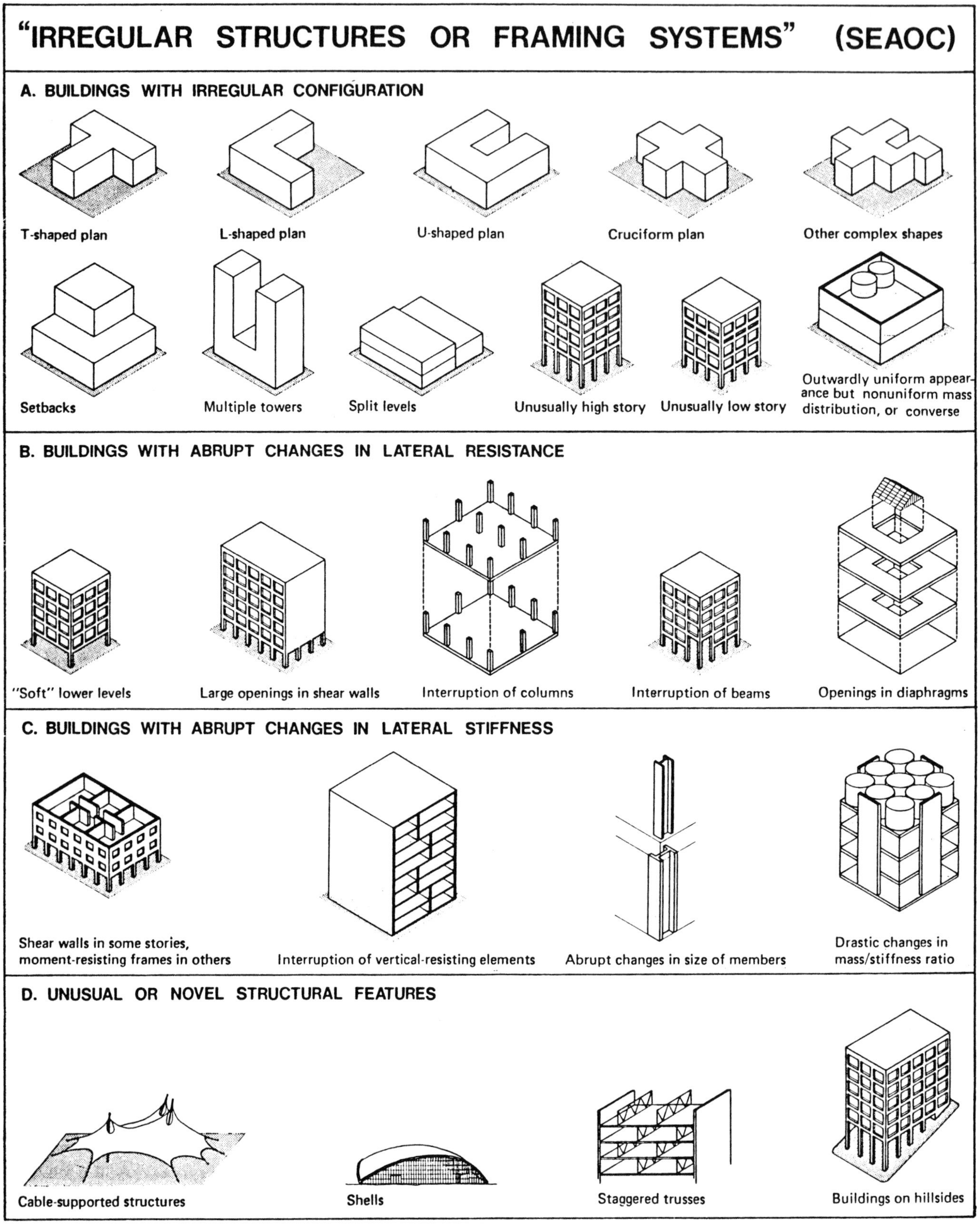

"IRREGULAR STRUCTURES OR FRAMING SYSTEMS" (SEAOC)

A. BUILDINGS WITH IRREGULAR CONFIGURATION

T-shaped plan   L-shaped plan   U-shaped plan   Cruciform plan   Other complex shapes

Setbacks   Multiple towers   Split levels   Unusually high story   Unusually low story   Outwardly uniform appearance but nonuniform mass distribution, or converse

B. BUILDINGS WITH ABRUPT CHANGES IN LATERAL RESISTANCE

"Soft" lower levels   Large openings in shear walls   Interruption of columns   Interruption of beams   Openings in diaphragms

C. BUILDINGS WITH ABRUPT CHANGES IN LATERAL STIFFNESS

Shear walls in some stories, moment-resisting frames in others   Interruption of vertical-resisting elements   Abrupt changes in size of members   Drastic changes in mass/stiffness ratio

D. UNUSUAL OR NOVEL STRUCTURAL FEATURES

Cable-supported structures   Shells   Staggered trusses   Buildings on hillsides

Figure 3.11: Graphic interpretation of "irregular structures or framing systems" from the Commentary to the SEAOC Recommended Lateral Force Requirements and Commentary.

It should also be noted that while the modal analysis will give a better definition of the problem, the problem is not alleviated. The 1990 Commentary to the SEAOC Lateral Force Requirements now includes an extensive discussion of the types of configuration irregularity, their effects and importance, and how they should be dealt with. (Appendix 1D5b, Irregularity and Setbacks) In some instances clauses have been added to the code which deal directly with a problem. But, in general, the solutions are design and concept oriented and still rely on the engineer's understanding and experience. Figure 3.11 is reprinted from the SEAOC Commentary.

These irregularities vary in importance as to their effect, and their influence also varies in degree, depending on which particular irregularity is present. Thus, while in an extreme form the re-entrant corner is a serious type of plan irregularity, in a lesser form it may have little significance. The determination of the point at which a given irregularity becomes serious used to be a matter of judgment, but the new codes now attempt to define the issue in a quantitative way.

However, the code determinations are as yet largely untested and somewhat controversial. In particular, the 5 story exception is open to question, and the ruling that configuration irregularities are not significant below that height is not borne out by practical experience. Thus the recent codification of irregularity does not relieve the designer from the responsibility of understanding the ways in which the irregularity impacts seismic performance.

While the irregularities shown in Figures 3.9 and 3.10 and 3.11 may serve as a checklist for ascertaining a problem configuration, four of the more serious configuration problems are described in detail in the sections below. In addition, some suggestions as to their solution are also provided, recognizing that it may not be possible to totally eliminate an undesirable configuration.

FOUR COMMON CONFIGURATION PROBLEMS

Soft First Stories

The most prominent of the set of problems caused by discontinuous strength and stiffness is the *soft story*. This term has commonly been applied to buildings whose ground level story, while adequate in strength, is less stiff than those above. The building code distinguishes between soft stories, discontinuities in stiffness and weak stories (discontinuities in **vertical** load capacity or strength). Structures with weak stories are limited by code to two stories or 30 feet in height. A soft story at any floor creates a problem, but since the forces are generally greatest towards the base of a building, a stiffness discontinuity between the first and second floors tends to result in the most serious condition. Three typical conditions create the soft first story. (Figure 3.12)

The problem that all these variations of the soft story share is that most of the earthquake forces in the building, and any consequent structural deformity, will tend to be concentrated in the weaker floor or at the point of discontinuity,

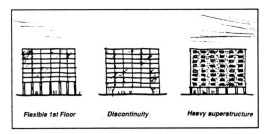

Figure 3.12: Three types of soft first stories

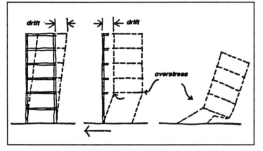

Figure 3.13: Soft story failure

instead of being more uniformly distributed among all the stories.

Instead of a building's deflection under horizontal forces being distributed equally among the upper floors, it is accommodated almost entirely in the first floor. Tremendous distortion in the floor, and stress concentration at the second floor connections, can cause failure at this line, resulting in the collapse or partial collapse of the upper floors. (Figure 3.13)

The best solution to the problem of the "soft" story is to avoid the discontinuity through architectural design. If, for some programmatic or compelling image reasons, this is not possible, the next step is to investigate ways of reducing the discontinuity by other means, such as increasing the number of columns or adding bracing. (Figure 3.14)

Discontinuous Shear Walls

When shear walls form the main lateral resisting elements of the building, they may be required to resist very high lateral forces. If these walls do not line up in plan from one floor to the next, the forces cannot flow directly down through the walls from roof to foundation, and the consequent indirect load path can result in serious overstressing at the points of discontinuity. Often this discontinuous shear wall condition represents a special, but common, case of the "soft" first story problem. The programmatic requirements for an open first floor may result in the elimination of the shear wall at that level, and its replacement by a frame.

A discontinuity in vertical stiffness and strength leads to a concentration of stresses and ultimately to damage and collapse, and the story which must hold up the remaining stories in a building should be the last, rather than the first, component to be sacrificed.

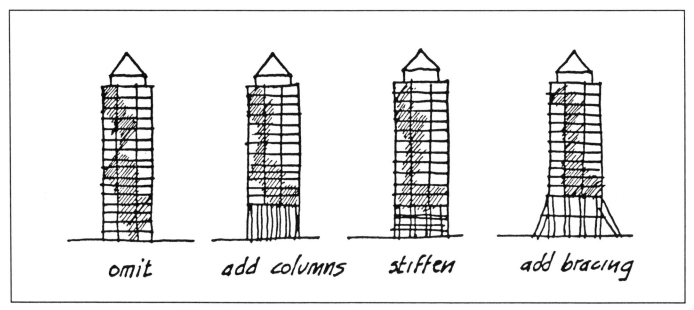

omit   add columns   stiffen   add bracing

Figure 3.14: Reducing discontinuity at a soft first story.

Figure 3.15: Soft first stories are a common form of earthquake-induced building failure, as in the Olive View Hospital.

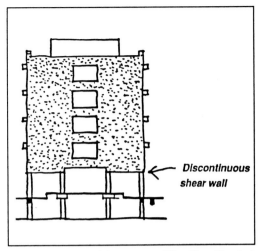

Figure 3.16: The soft first story at Olive View Hospital, showing the discontinuity between the "soft" framed lower levels and the stiff shear wall structure above.

Olive View Hospital, which was severely damaged in the 1971 San Fernando, California earthquake, represents an extreme form of the discontinuous shear wall problem. (Figure 3.15) The general vertical configuration of the main building was a "soft" two-story layer of rigid frames on which was supported a four story (five, including the penthouse) stiff, shear wall-plus-frame structure. (Figure 3.16) The second floor extended out to form a large plaza. The severe damage occurred in the soft story portion, which is to be expected. The upper stories moved as a unit, and moved so much that the columns at ground level could not accommodate such a huge displacement between their bases and tops and hence failed. The largest amount a column was left permanently out-of-plumb was 2-1/2 *feet!*

The solution to the problem of discontinuous shear walls is unequivocally to eliminate the condition. To do this may create architectural problems of planning, circulation or image. If this is so, then this clearly indicates that the decision to use shear walls as resistant elements was wrong from the inception of the design. Conversely, if the decision is made to use shear walls, then their presence must be recognized from the beginning of schematic design, and their size and location must be the subject of careful architectural and engineering coordination.

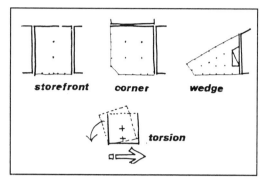

Figure 3.17: Variations in perimeter strength and stiffness

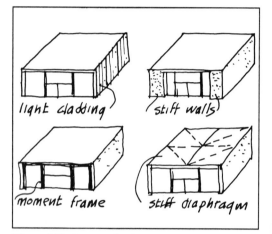

Figure 3.18: Structural solutions to resist torsion

Variations in Perimeter Strength and Stiffness

This problem may occur in buildings whose configuration is geometrically regular and symmetrical, but nonetheless irregular for seismic design purposes.

A building's seismic behavior is strongly influenced by the nature of the perimeter design. If there is wide variation in strength and stiffness around the perimeter, the center of mass will not coincide with the center of resistance, and torsional forces will tend to cause the building to rotate around the center of resistance. This effect is illustrated in Figure 3.17.

Open front design is common in buildings such as stores, fire stations and motor maintenance shops, where it is necessary to provide large doors for the passage of vehicles. The problem can be particularly acute when the open front is asymmetrical, as in a corner, or wedge shape building. The large imbalance in perimeter strength and stiffness around the building can result in large torsional forces.

The purpose of any solution to this problem is to reduce the possibility of torsion. Four possible alternative strategies are shown in Figure 3.18.

The first strategy is to design a frame structure of approximately equal strength and stiffness for the entire perimeter. The opaque portion of the perimeter can be constructed of nonstructural cladding, designed so that it does not affect the seismic performance of the frame. This can be done either by using lightweight cladding, or by ensuring that heavy materials, such as concrete or masonry, are isolated from the frame.

A second approach is to increase the stiffness of the open facades by adding shear walls at or near the open face.

A third solution is to use a very strong moment-resistant or braced frame at the open front, which approaches the solid wall in stiffness. The ability to do this will be dependent on the size of the facades: a long steel frame can never compare to a long concrete wall in stiffness. This is, however, a good solution for wood frame structures, such as apartment houses with ground floor garage areas, because even a comparatively long steel frame can be made as stiff as plywood shear walls.

Finally, the possibility of torsion may be accepted and the structure designed to accept it, with careful analysis of the diaphragm design and its ability to transfer forces back to an inadequate resisting structural system. This solution will apply only to relatively small structures with stiff diaphragms, which can be designed to act as a unit.

Seismological Society of America

Figure 3.20: Collapse of re-entrant corner of the L-shaped San Marco Building, 1925 Santa Barbara, California earthquake.

Figure 3.19: Re-entrant corner configurations

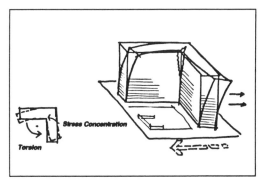

Figure 3.21: Problems with the L-shaped building

Re-entrant Corners

The re-entrant corner is the common characteristic of building forms that, in plan, assume the shape of an L,T,H, etc., or a combination of these shapes.

This is a most useful and traditional set of building shapes, which enable large plan areas to be accommodated in relatively compact form, yet still provide a high percentage of perimeter rooms with access to air and light.

These configurations, pictured in Figure 3.19, are so common and familiar that the fact that they represent one of the most difficult problem areas in seismic design may seem surprising. Examples of damage to re-entrant corner type buildings are common, and this problem was one of the first to be identified by observers. (Figure 3.20)

There are two problems created by these shapes. The first is that they tend to produce variations of rigidity, and hence differential motions between different portions of the building, resulting in a local stress concentration at the re-entrant corner. This effect is shown in Figure 3.21.

The second problem of this form is torsion. This is caused because the center of mass and the center of rigidity in this form cannot geometrically coincide for all possible earthquake directions. The result is rotation, that will tend to distort the building in ways that will vary in nature and magnitude depending on the characteristics of the ground motion. The resulting forces are very difficult to analyze and predict.

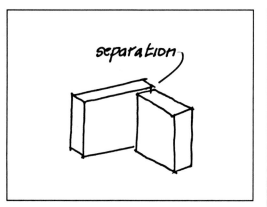

Figure 3.22: Structurally separate the building into simple shapes.

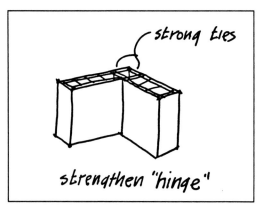

Figure 3.23: Tie the building together more strongly.

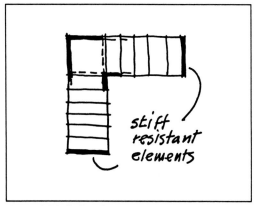

Figure 3.24: Stiffen the free ends of the building.

The stress concentration at the "notch" and the torsional effects are interrelated. The magnitude of the forces and the seriousness of the problem will depend on:

- the mass of the building,
- the structural system,
- the length of the wings and their aspect ratios, and
- the height of the wings and their height/depth ratios.

There are two basic alternative approaches to the problem of the re-entrant corner forms: structurally to separate the building into simpler shapes, or to tie the building together more strongly. (Figure 3.22 and 3.23) When Frank Lloyd Wright divided the Tokyo Imperial Hotel into a number of rectangular blocks he was adopting the former solution. Once the decision is made to use separation joints, they must be designed and constructed correctly to achieve the original intent. Structurally separated entities of a building must be fully capable of resisting vertical and lateral forces on their own, and their individual configurations must be balanced horizontally and vertically.

To design a separation joint, the maximum **drift** of the two units must be calculated by the structural consultant. The worst case is when the two individual structures would lean toward each other simultaneously, and hence the sum of the dimension of the separation space must allow for the sum of the building drifts.

Several considerations arise if it is decided to dispense with the separation joint and tie the building together. Collectors at the intersection can transfer forces across the intersection area, but only if the design allows for these beam-like members to extend straight across without interruption. Even better than collectors, are full-height continuous walls in this same location.

Since the portion of the wing which typically distorts the most is the free end, it is desirable to place stiffening elements at that location to reduce its response. (Figure 3.24)

The use of splayed rather than right angle re-entrant corners lessens the stress concentration at the notch. (Figure 3.25) This is analogous to the way a rounded hole in a steel plate creates less stress concentration than a rectangular hole, or the way a tapered beam is structurally more desirable than an abruptly notched one.

THE BOTTOM LINE

Configuration problems originate in the schematic design of the building: a good or bad configuration is the architect's contribution to seismic performance. If the configuration is good the seismic design will be simple and economical and good performance is more likely to be assured. If the configuration is bad the seismic design will be expensive and good performance will be less than certain.

This is not to say that all buildings should be symmetrical cubes. The architect has many agendas, of which meeting seismic requirements is but one. But understanding the problems caused by configuration irregularities will go a long way towards assuring feasible solutions, and early consultation between the architect and engineer should be directed toward creative compromise rather than adversarial stubbornness.

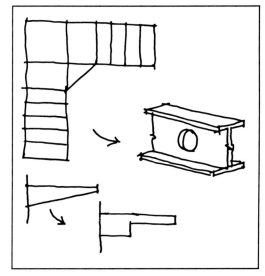

Figure 3.25: Use splayed rather than right angle re-entrant corners.

Chapter 4: Seismically Resistant Structural Systems

BASIC SEISMIC ENGINEERING CONCEPTS

Traditionally, structural engineers have equated the designed capacity of a structure with the loads imposed on it (live loads, wind loads, thermal loads, etc.). Appropriate safety factors are used which ensure that the materials never exceed the elastic range of behavior. Doing this, we are assured that the structure will behave in the manner predicted by the designer.

But in earthquake regions, we have a confused tradition which is an outgrowth of the concept of treating earthquake loads as static, similar to winds. By doing this, and by initially assuming that earthquakes can be represented by lateral loads similar in magnitude to wind forces, we have evolved a simple concept, but one which significantly understates the possible earthquake forces. The result is that a structure conventionally and statically designed by the usual elastic behavior concepts is underdesigned for the real earthquake forces it may experience and may, of necessity, have greater demands that force it to perform in the inelastic or non-linear range. In this range, structural behavior is neither predictable nor well understood.

The obvious, and simplistic, solution to overcome the discrepancy between capacity and demand is to increase the minimum code seismic loads to insure elastic behavior in all earthquakes. However, this approach cannot be economically justified based on current knowledge of building performance under earthquake loads.

So we have a unique situation in seismic design, where we do not design the structure for the anticipated loads but rather try to rationalize the performance by understanding the complex phenomena of non-linear behavior, ductility and energy absorption and dissipation.

Figure 4.1 illustrates the difference between the actual earthquake spectra (upper curves) and the building code elastic design basis (lower curves). The difference is substantial, and not all building systems are capable of meeting the actual earthquake demand; when the discrepancy is unresolved, structural failure results.

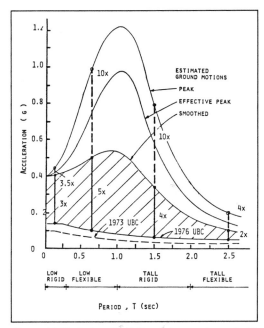

Figure 4.1: Variation of building resistance demand with estimated ground motion

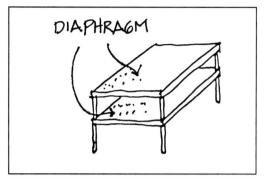

Figure 4.2: Diaphragms are the prime horizontal resisting system.

Figure 4.3: Horizontal diaphragms typically fail at their connections to vertical resisting elements.

RESISTANT SYSTEMS

In designing to resist seismic forces, the structural engineer uses a relatively small vocabulary of components which are combined to form a complete resistance system.

In the vertical plane three kinds of components resist lateral forces: shear walls, braced frames, and moment resisting frames (sometimes called "rigid frames"). In the horizontal plane diaphragms are used, generally formed by the floor and roof planes of the building, or by horizontal trusses. (Figures 4.2 and 4.3) These elements are also the basic architectural components of the building.

Diaphragms

The term "diaphragm" is used to identify horizontal resistance elements (generally floors and roofs) that act to transfer lateral forces between vertical resistance elements (shear walls or frames). The diaphragm acts as a horizontal beam: the diaphragm itself acts as the web of the beam, and its edges act as flanges. (Figure 4.4)

Floors and roofs often have to be penetrated - by staircases, elevator or duct shafts, skylights, or other architectural or mechanical features. The size and

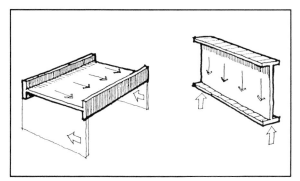

Figure 4.4: Diaphragms act like horizontal beams.

location of these penetrations is critical to the effectiveness of the diaphragms. The reason for this is not hard to see when the diaphragm is visualized as a beam: we can, for example, easily see that openings cut in the tension flange of this beam will seriously weaken its load carrying capabilitity. (Figure 4.5)

Collectors, or "drag struts," are diaphragm framing members which "collect" or "drag" diaphragm shear forces from laterally unsupported areas to vertical resisting elements.

The location of a hole (core, skylight, etc.) at the intersection of the component rectangles would interrupt the collector's load path (Figure 4.6), and hence should be avoided.

Shear Walls

Vertical cantilever walls which are designed to receive lateral forces from diaphragms and transmit them to the ground are commonly termed *shear walls*. The forces in these walls are predominantly shear forces, though a slender wall will also incur significant bending. (Figure 4.7)

Figure 4.8 shows a simple building with shear walls at its ends. Ground motion enters the building and creates inertial forces which move the floor diaphragms. This movement is resisted by the shear walls, and the forces are transmitted back down to the foundation.

If the building is visualized as rotated so that it extends horizontally, it is clear that the shear walls are acting as cantilever girders which support beams represented by the floor diaphragms.

The size and location of shear walls are extremely critical. Plans can be conceived of as collections of resistant elements which have varying orientations to oppose translational forces, and which are placed at varying distances from the center of rigidity to resist torsional forces.

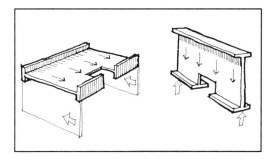

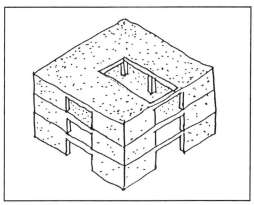

Figures 4.5 and 4.6: Holes in beams or in diaphragms, interrupt structural continuity.

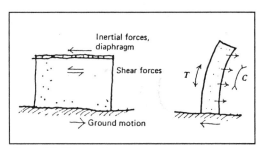

Figure 4.7: Shear walls

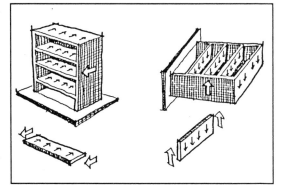

Figure 4.8: Shear walls are like cantilever girders when resisting seismic forces.

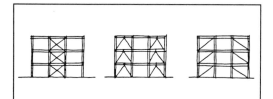

Figure 4.9: Typical bracing configuration

Christopher Arnold

Figure 4.11: Moment resistant frames are typically steel structures with stiff welded joints.

Braced Frames

Braced frames act in the same manner as shear walls though they may be of lower resistance and stiffness depending on their detailed design. Vibrating forces may cause the bracing to elongate or compress, in which case it loses its effectiveness and permits large deformations or collapse of the vertical structure. Bracing can be designed in a variety of configurations, depending on the forces to be resisted and on architectural limitations. It generally takes the form of steel rolled sections, circular bar sections, or tubes. (Figure 4.9)

Detailing to ensure complete load paths for the high forces is very important, and detailing which causes eccentricity may greatly reduce the effectiveness of bracing.

Moment Resistant Frames

When seismic resistance is provided by *moment resistant frames,* lateral forces are resisted by rotations of the beam/column joints. This induces shear and bending forces in the frame members. The joints become highly stressed, and their design and construction becomes critical. (Figure 4.10) In addition, behavior of the frame in the inelastic, or plastic, range becomes an important feature in resistance strategy, by using the energy absorption obtained by the ductility of the structure prior to ultimate failure. For this reason moment resistant frames are generally conceived as steel structures with stiff welded joints, in which the natural ductility of the material is of advantage. However, properly reinforced concrete frames will also act as ductile frames: that is, they will retain some resistance capacity in the inelastic range, prior to failure.

The use of moment resistant frames is of architectural significance in two ways. One is that their use obviates the need for shear walls or braced frames, with the possible restrictive planning implications of both. The other is that moment resisting frame structures tend to be much more flexible than shear wall type structures, with consequent implications for the design of accompanying architectural elements such as curtain walls, partitions, and ceilings. (Figure 4.11)

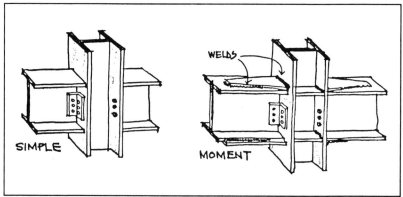

Figure 4.10: Joints are critical in moment resistant frames.

New and Emerging Resistant Systems

Shear walls can be constructed of masonry (and have been for ages), reinforced concrete, plywood or wood boards, and even of steel plates. Diagonal braces have been made of timbers, steel tension rods or steel compression members, and of reinforced concrete bracing struts. Reliable moment resisting frames have evolved with technological improvements in both welding of steel and confinement of concrete by steel reinforcing. Recently, however, several new concepts, which are combinations and variations of the basic three, have evolved. These new concepts acknowledge the need for ductility and energy dissipation. Some notable new systems are:

1. *Eccentric Bracing*, which combines the ductility of the moment frame with the rigidity, or drift control, of the conventional brace.
2. *Dual Moment-Frame/Shear Wall*, combines ductility with rigidity.
3. *Progressive Resistance Systems*, which combine two or three systems that progress in load-carrying capacity from rigidity to ductility at predetermined load levels.
4. *Base isolation*, in which the superstructure of the building is partially isolated from ground motion by the use of bearings, generally of specially formulated rubber or rubber and steel laminates. The superstructure must, still, be designed using conventional seismic resistant methods, but the force to be resisted will be substantially reduced.

It is useful to understand when these various structural systems evolved. **Table 4.A** gives approximate times when individual types of construction were generally used in California. Not all were intentionally used for seismic

Table 4.A

		HISTORY OF SEISMIC RESISTING STRUCTURAL SYSTEMS			
Time	**Bearing Walls**	**Building Frame**	**Moment Frame**	**Dual System**	**Controlled Behavior**
1800	Adobe Timber Frame Masonry (Timber Frame)				
1900	Masonry (Steel Frame)	Steel Frame (Masonry Walls)			
1910	Concrete Walls and Framing	Concrete Frame and Walls			
1920		Steel Frame (Concrete Walls)	Steel Frame (Ordinary)		
1930			Concrete Frame (Ordinary)	Steel Frame and Concrete Shear Walls	
1940	Concrete Walls (Light Framing)				
1950			Steel (Ductile)	X-Braced and Steel Frame	
1960	RGBM or CMU (Light Framing)	X-Braced Steel Frame (Light Walls)	Concrete (Ductile)		
1970	Ductile Shear Walls			Steel Frame and Steel Walls Progressive Resistance System	
1980					Eccentric Braces
1990					*Isolation System *Passive Dampers
	* Evolving Systems				

Christopher Arnold

Figure 4.12: New structural concepts evolve in response to the performance failures of preceding systems.

resistance; it is only since about 1960 that specific systems have evolved to meet the unique needs generated by the earthquake problem. Special details were developed for ductile reinforced concrete moment frames in the 1960s; economic steel braced frames were perfected in the late 1970s, and base isolation concepts and details are currently being developed in the 1990s.

As new concepts evolve, some old ones cease to be used, either for economic or technical reasons. It is also important to note that some of the old systems, such as unreinforced masonry infill around a simple structural steel frame, used from the 1890s to 1920 and now abandoned, did perform well. On the other hand, the concept of dual systems with brittle energy dissipation material contained by ductile steel, which once proved successful, are now being reconsidered, especially in retrofit applications. (Figure 4.12)

BUILDING RESPONSE

It is most important to be able to understand and predict a building's earthquake reponse. Will it perform well relative to other buildings? Will it yield and crack, but be repairable? Will it be severely damaged, but not collapse? It is essential to be able to accurately predict earthquake behavior.

Table 4.B provides a subjective view of seismic behavior of various structural systems based on earthquake observations and laboratory testing. Some interesting and surprising observations should be noted. First, many of our new and highly regarded moment frame buildings have not been tested by an actual earthquake. Second, although the old nominal steel frame infilled with unreinforced masonry walls performed very well in San Francisco in 1906, we have abandoned its use because we no longer build that way, and because we have difficulty modeling and analyzing that kind of composite construction.

SELECTING A STRUCTURAL SYSTEM

Key Factors

The selection of an appropriate structural system for a building located in a region of moderate to high seismicity is a complex task. It is a problem that must be shared by the owner, architect and stuctural engineer if a successful product is to result. The issue is made complex because the response to random earthquake motions of both the structural framework, the entire building shell, and the contents is only just begnning to be properly understood. The problem is confused by the numerous variables and thousands of combinations of important factors, and by occasional inappropriate solutions.

Selection of any structural solution must be made by an informed design team, and this is particularly important in a seismic region. The factors which must be evaluated for seismic regions are:

SUMMARY OF SEISMIC PERFORMANCE OF STRUCTURAL SYSTEMS

Structural System	EQ Performance	Test Data	Specific Bldg. Perf. & Energy Absorption	General Comments
Wood Frame	SF 1906, etc. ALA 1964 Variable to *Good*	1950's DFPA etc.	· SF Bldgs. performed reasonably well even though not detailed. · Energy Absorption is excellent.	· Connection details are critical. · Configuration is significant.
Unreinforced Masonry Wall	SF 1906 SB 1925 LB 1933 LA 1994 Variable to *Poor*	? Recent SEADSC	· Unreinf. masonry has performed poorly when *not* tied together. · Energy absorption is good if system integrity is maintained.	· Continuity and ties between walls and diaphragm is essential.
Steel Frame w/Mas Infill	SF 1906 Variable to *Good*	?	· SF Bldgs. performed very well. · Energy absorption is excellent.	· Bldg. form must be uniform, relatively small bay sizes.
R/C Wall	SF 1957 ALA 1964 JAPAN 1966 LA 1994 Variable to *Poor*	?	· Bldgs. in Alaska, SF and Japan performed poorly w/spandrel and pier failure · Brittle system.	· Proportion of spandrel and piers is critical, detail for ductility and shear.
Steel Brace	SF 1906 TAFT 1952 LA 1994 Variable	Univ. of Mich. Japan UCB	· Major braced systems performed well. · Minor bracing and tension braces performed poorly.	· Details and proportions are critical.
Steel Moment Frame	LA 1971 JAPAN 1978 LA 1994 ? *Good*	Lehigh UCB	· LA and Japanese Bldgs. 1971/78 performed well. · Energy absorption is excellent · LA 1994, mixed performance	· Both conventional and D.F. have performed well if designed for drift.
Concrete S.W.	CARAC 1965 ALA 1964 LA 1971 ALG. 1980 *Variable*	PCA U. of Ill. UCB	· Poor performance w/ discontinuous walls. · San Francisco, Alaska, Algeria, Caracas. · Uneven energy absorp.	· *Configuration* is *critical,* soft story or L-shape w/torsion have produced failures.
P/C Concrete	ALA 1964 BULGARIA 1978 SF 1980 LA 1994 Variable to *Poor*	Japan ?	· Poor performance in 1964, 1978, 1980, 1994 · Brittle Failure	· Details for continuity are critical. · *Ductility* must be achieved.
R/C DMF	LA 1971 ? *Good*	PCA Texas Toronto UCB	· Good perf. in 1971, LA. · System will crack. · Energy absorption is good. · Mixed performance in 1994 LA	· Details *critical.*

Table 4.B

Christopher Arnold

Figure 4.13: The design team must ask if the goal for building performance is lifesafety, property protection or continued function after the earthquake.

1. the anticipated level of *earthquake ground motion;*
2. the *site geology* and its impact on the structure;
3. the *building occupancy* and its impact on building form and structural system;
4. the *building configuration,* which may be arbitrary or dictated by site, zoning, or program;
5. the *structural system* relative to the configuration;
6. the *structural details;*
7. *nonstructural components* (cladding, ceilings, partitions, etc.) in relation to the primary structure; and
8. *construction quality* and its impact on structural continuity.

Each of these issues is important, to varying degrees, for specific buildings. A tall structure, for example, will require a dominance of the structural framework, and consequently will usually have a clarity of structural concept and performance. In contrast, a low 2- or 3-story building may have the structural framework compromised to achieve a unique but irrational form. The seismic performance may not be satisfactory unless a significant amount of creative collaboration is involved to overcome the decision to use the irrational form.

Goals

Because the range of options can be so varied when designing a building to resist an earthquake, it is first essential to establish goals for the project. This must usually be done with the mutual agreement of the owner and the full design team, and is a necessary step because simple compliance with the minimum provisions of the building code does not assure success in an earthquake. To establish the project goal, we must ask what the final result is to be: Life safety? Property protection? Or continued post-earthquake function? (Figure 4.13)

The seismic requirements stated in most building codes are intended only to assure life safety. To achieve this, only the primary structures must be protected to prevent collapse. With this goal, nonstructural elements may be sacrificed, and structural damage incurred even though substantial economic loss will result. In contrast, to protect the building from damage usually requires an upgrading from the minimum code loads and concepts, and total building performance must be understood. The lateral movement of the structural frame and its impact on partitions, cladding and equipment must be addressed. The high accelerations experienced in a flexible, but strong, ductile steel frame must be translated to strong appropriate mountings for cladding and contents to minimize damage. This is clearly a different level of design and construction effort, and will be more expensive than a minimum code solution.

An even higher level of performance is required by some building owners, who require continued post-earthquake function without damage or disruption. Frequently computer facilities, laboratories and, in California, hospitals, are designed to this performance level. To achieve this goal, a sophisticated building system is required; one with coordination between design concepts, construction details and even user attitudes.

FINAL CONSIDERATIONS

Selecting a system which will perform well is, therefore, a demanding task. The goals must be established; a joint effort of architects and engineers is required to evolve a building form responsive to the program; site characteristics and seismicity must be considered; a structure compatible with the above issues needs to be selected and analyzed; and, finally, the details must be developed.

There are hundreds of structural system combinations to choose from. Figure 4.14 shows several generic locations for structural elements. Which one is appropriate for a given project? Do you select the one in current favor? Or the one you used on the previous project? Or do you invent a new idea based on current research? The answer is a combination of the above. Consideration

Figure 4.14: Generic locations for seismic resisting structural elements.

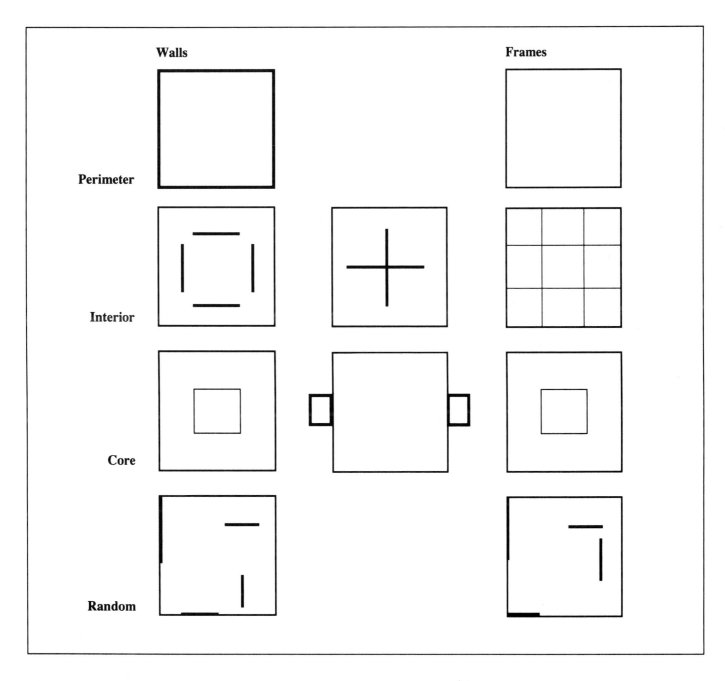

Figures 4.15 and 4.16: Even simple traditional framing systems must be well analyzed and engineered to respond effectively to seismic forces.

must always be given to the unique requirements of the project, the site, the occupancy, the geometry, the anticipated life of the building. Several of these issues are translated into structural systems in **Table 4.C**, where site conditions and occupancy issues are listed.

The structural resisting systems must be well understood to develop creative and reliable solutions. (Figures 4.15 and 4.16) The engineer can now use the conventional or static systems which rely on uncontrolled yielding or fracture to satisfy the earthquake demand, or use the new energy dissipation concepts discussed below. These structural systems must be paired with each configuration (and building program) to complete the solution. Structures can be "tuned" to overcome some adverse situations, such as re-entrant corner buildings, but tuning will not overcome major problems.

Flexible steel moment frames are economical but rely on lateral deformation to dissipate seismic energy. Recent post-earthquake observations of a well designed 12-story steel frame in San Jose, California, confirmed this behavior; however, several negative aspects became apparent and reinforced concerns about flexible steel frames. The building continued to vibrate at large amplitudes at its fundamental period of 2.0 seconds for 60 seconds after the ground motion stopped. The building was dissipating energy with very little damping. The result of this undamped vibration was severe internal damage to furniture and contents at the upper stories. So we have a clear example of successful structural performance without damage to the steel frame, but unsuccessful performance of the building contents and great trauma for the occupants. The implications of this performance data are significant and may alter our feelings about preferred systems.

Alternatives to the steel moment frame are those systems which introduce some rigidity to limit lateral drift and corresponding nonstructural damage. Braced frames introduce more stiffness and rigidity. Shear walls are very stiff, but must be designed to higher forces. They will tend to directly transmit ground motion forces with an abrupt motion, but they are also less likely to develop resonance and to amplify the motion. If the building requires a number of walls for planning purposes - as most residential buildings do - then shear walls are an economical solution.

Dual systems using steel walls or braces combined with ductile moment frames, or ductile eccentric steel braced frames, offer the advantages of ductility and drift control. Other alternatives are buildings with specific energy dissipation mechanisms: controlled capacity shear links, friction systems, flexural beams, or base isolators.

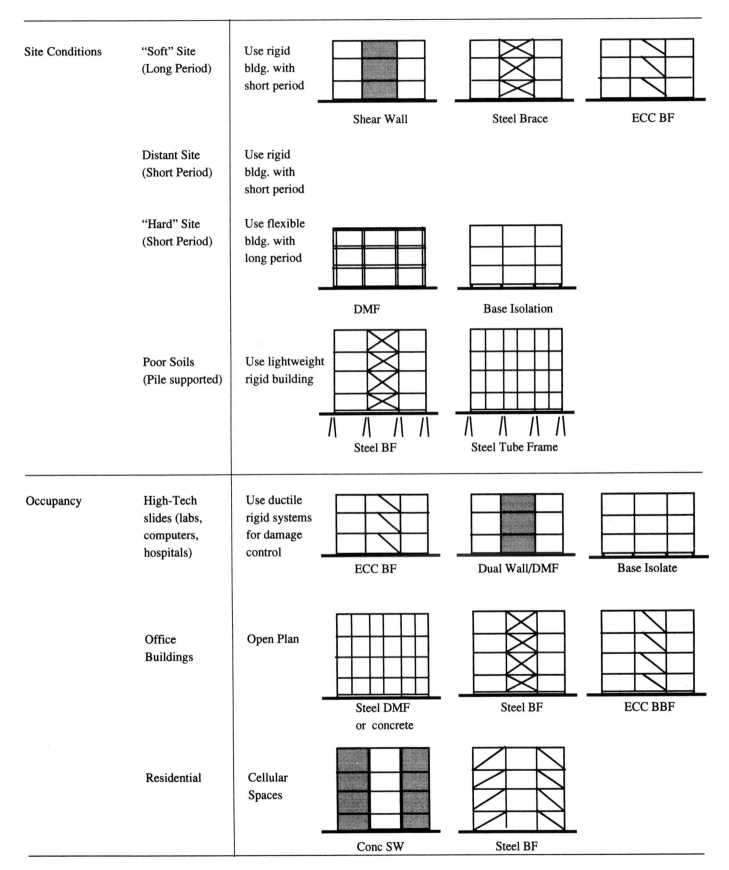

Site Conditions	"Soft" Site (Long Period)	Use rigid bldg. with short period	Shear Wall	Steel Brace	ECC BF
	Distant Site (Short Period)	Use rigid bldg. with short period			
	"Hard" Site (Short Period)	Use flexible bldg. with long period	DMF	Base Isolation	
	Poor Soils (Pile supported)	Use lightweight rigid building	Steel BF	Steel Tube Frame	
Occupancy	High-Tech slides (labs, computers, hospitals)	Use ductile rigid systems for damage control	ECC BF	Dual Wall/DMF	Base Isolate
	Office Buildings	Open Plan	Steel DMF or concrete	Steel BF	ECC BBF
	Residential	Cellular Spaces	Conc SW	Steel BF	

Table 4.C: Structural system options

Chapter 5: The Basics Of Seismic Codes

BUILDING CODES AND SEISMIC PROVISIONS

The first seismic building code to be developed in the United States was the seismic portion of the Uniform Building Code (UBC) published by the International Conference of Building Officials (ICBO) in California. The seismic provisions of the UBC were developed on a volunteer basis by the Structural Engineers Association of California (SEAOC). Currently, in addition to the UBC, the following are important seismic codes in use:

- BOCA National Building Code
- SBCCI Standard Building Code
- GSA (Federal Buildings)
- Tri-services (Department of Defense-Military)
- Title 24, California (Hospitals and Schools)
- Veterans Administration (Veterans Hospitals)
- State Historic Building Code (SHBC) [California]
- City of Los Angeles, Section 88 (Existing URM Buildings)
- Uniform Code for Building Conservation (UCBC)

Most of the codes listed above have the stated goal of maintaining life safety; only Title 24 (California) has a higher performance goal of damage control to maintain post-earthquake function in hospitals. The last three listings, which relate to existing buildings, permit lower design force levels than those required for new buildings. (Figure 5.1)

Starting in the mid-1970s the Federal Government initiated a research program to develop a state-of-the-art approach to a seismic code that would have nationwide applicability. This effort resulted in the 1978 publication of the ATC-3 document (named after the Applied Technology Council, the non-profit engineering research group that developed it). Subsequently, the document has undergone several revisions and is now known as the *National Earthquake Hazards Reduction Program: Recommended Provisions for the Development of Seismic Regulations for New Buildings* or the *NEHRP Provisions*. Published by the Building Seismic Safety Council in Washington, and updated on a 3-year basis, the *NEHRP Provisions* document is not a code, but a technical resource document to assist in code development. In format, language and content, however, the document is very similar to a seismic code.

Figure 5.1: Advances in building code seismic provisions are intended to ensure life safety and prevent the types of failure and collapse that occur in pre-code buildings.

SUMMARY OF BUILDING CODE SEISMIC DESIGN CONCEPTS		
	Uniform Building Code(1991)	NEHRP Provisions(1991)
Goal	Life Safety	Life Safety
Seismic Load	Base Shear V (F=MA concept) $V = \dfrac{ZICW}{R_w}$ $(C = \dfrac{1.25S}{T^{2/3}})$	Base Shear V (F=MA Concept) $V = C_s W$ $(C_s = \dfrac{1.2A_vS}{RT^{2/3}})$
Zone	Z 5 Zones 0.075, 0.15, 0.20, 0.30, 0.40	6 Zones 0.05, 0.10, 0.15, 0.20, 0.30, 0.40
Import-ance	I Building Occupancy (1.0, 1.25)	SHEG Exposure Groups (3 categories) and SPC Performance Categories (5 categories)

Struct. Response	R_w Response Modifications
	     based on 5 basic Structural types
		R Response Modifications
		     based on 6 basic Structural types

Soil	S 4 Soil Profiles
	     (1.0, 1.2, 1.5, 2.0)
		S 4 Soil Profiles
		     (1.0, 1.2, 1.5, 2.0)

Mass	W Building Weight	W Building Weight
Period	T Building Period	T Building Period

Table 5.A

Table 5.A shows a comparison between the basic provisions of the 1991 UBC and the 1991 *NEHRP Provisions*. This summary shows that these two codes are very similar in concept and in the factors that are included.

Prior to 1988, the UBC and the *NEHRP Provisions* tended to pursue somewhat diverging approaches to code development and modification. However, in the 1988 edition of the UBC and the *NEHRP Provisions*, a notable merging of some concepts in the two documents occurred. While updating these documents continues independently, the concepts within them are subject to constant mutual review. Taken together, the SEAOC and NEHRP efforts represent probably the most influential and consistent effort in the world to provide a technical basis for seismic code development.

The UBC represents only one of the commonly used model codes in the U.S. The BOCA model code, developed by the Building Officials and Code Administrators organization is used extensively in the East and Midwest, and the Standard Building Code, developed by the Southern Building Code Congress International, is used extensively in the Southern states.

Until recently, the two latter model building codes groups have lagged behind in the development of seismic codes, primarily because these model codes were used in areas of little perceived seismic hazard. Concern for the seismic hazard present in other states in the U.S. besides California has resulted in a new interest in the development and adoption of appropriate codes, an interest which the development of the *NEHRP Provisions* was intended to support. Consequently, both the BOCA model code and the Standard Building Code now incorporate slightly modified versions of the *NEHRP Provisions* in their model building codes. (Figure 5.2)

Thus, on a national basis, the seismic code issue is basically accommodated by variations of the two main technical documents; the *NEHRP Provisions* and the UBC (or, more precisely, the SEAOC provisions upon which it is based.)

APPLYING CODES

The primary purpose of seismic building codes is to provide a simple uniform method to determine the seismic forces for any location with enough accuracy to ensure a safe and economical design. The code needs to provide for approximate uniformity of results so that no building owner, building type, or materials supplier is unfairly discriminated against.

In Chapter 1 it was shown that the earthquake forces on a building can be referred back to the basic formula for inertial forces - *F equals MA. M* is easy to obtain by calculating the weight of the building. How about *A*, the acceleration?

The *NEHRP Provisions* provide a number of sets of maps of the United States: these provide contour lines, or color codes of the counties in each state, so that the entire country is divided into seven areas. (Figure 5.3 shows a small scale reproduction of one of the maps provided with the *Provisions*.) Each area in turn is equivalent to a number from *0.05 to 0.40* in steps of *0.05, 0.10, 0.15, 0.20, 0.30,* and *0.40*. These represent *accelerations* in percentages of G - so that 0.40 represents 40% of G. This is the *A* for the *F = MA* formula. It's not quite as simple as that, but nevertheless the relationship of the maps to the fundamental formula is quite direct and clear.

These maps reflect a number of assumptions. The general criterion is that the risk at any location has only a *10 percent probability of being exceeded in 50 years,* which translates into a *mean recurrence interval of 475 years.* This is a statistical number and not a prediction: the important thing is that the map is expressing a uniform risk, so that by looking at the different numbers you get an approximation of the relative risk among different regions of the country.

The *Provisions* state that, for most instances the horizontal force on the building can be represented as a horizontal shear force trying to push the base of the building across the ground where the building is attached to its foundation. This force is called the *base shear*, and a formula is provided for its estimation. Application of this formula is a key part of the code methodology and is called

Figure 5.2: Seismic code provisions have undergone continuous development since the 1950's in response to both damaging earthquakes and to advances in engineering science.

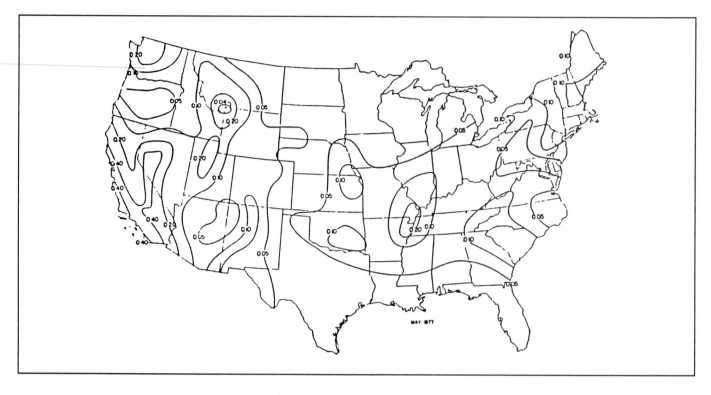

Figure 5.3: Contour map for coefficient A$_a$ for the continental United States.*

the *equivalent lateral force procedure*. This general methodology is characteristic of all seismic codes throughout the world.

In the *Provisions* this formula is $V=C_sW$ where:

C_s = the seismic design coefficient, which is related to an "expansion" of A, the acceleration number. The expansion adds other coefficients, or multipliers, which represent some of the other factors discussed in Chapter 1.

W = the building weight, which can easily be calculated.

$$C_s = 1.2A_v S/RT^{2/3}$$

where A$_v$ is obtained from the contour map.*

S is the Coefficient for *soil profile type* (i.e. relating to soil amplification). This is obtained from a table in the *Provisions*. The coefficient varies from 1 to 2.0. For poor ground, where the coefficient is 2.0, the acceleration number is multiplied by two, thus increasing the *design force* - the forces for which the building must be designed.

R is a *response modification* coefficient, relating to the type and ductility of the chosen structural system. R factors are also obtained from a table in the *Provisions*. This is a number from 1.25 to 8: it is a divisor, so it has the

---

*A$_v$ and A$_a$ are two slightly different expressions of the acceleration factor used for design, and separate maps are provided for each in the *Provisions*.

effect of reducing the design forces, and the higher the number, the higher the reduction.

T is the *period* of the building (simple formulae for estimating this are provided in the *Provisions.*)

It can be seen that these coefficients, **A, W, S, R,** and **T** encompass most of the characteristics discussed in Chapters 1 and 3 that affect the building's earthquake performance.

For a really simple way of establishing the seismic force, the Equivalent Lateral Force method provides an alternative equation that can be used at the designer's option. This is:

$$C_s = \frac{2.5A_a}{R}$$

Note that to use this equation it is not necessary to calculate the building period or estimate the soil type. Use of this equation will generally result in a larger force factor; for a small structure, such as a house, this is not usually significant.

In addition to the equivalent lateral force equation, a formula is provided for calculating the *vertical distribution* of forces that makes some allowance for possible amplification, and allocates a higher proportion of the forces to the upper floors of the building.

Application of the equivalent lateral force formula to locations of maximum shaking (i.e: A_a=0.40 on the map) produces a coefficient C_s that varies approximately from *0.125* for a steel moment resistant frame building to *0.80* for an unreinforced masonry building. (Figure 5.4)

In other words, an unreinforced masonry building, which is a very poor seismic force resisting structure, would have to be designed to resist a base shear force equal to *80% of its weight* - a very high acceleration. (In fact, unreinforced masonry structures are not permitted to be constructed in California, and it would be very difficult, if not impossible, to design an unreinforced masonry structure for these forces). On the other hand, a moment resisting frame would only have to be designed to resist lateral forces equal to *12 1/2 % of its weight.*

So the equivalent lateral force equation provides a simple mathematical formula by which most of the factors that determine the lateral force on the building can be accounted for in a uniform way. Moreover, since the code defines a minimum force level, any of these coefficients can be revised upwards if the owner wishes to obtain a higher level of protection. This is a common practice.

Other parts of the *Provisions* set limits on *drift*, require the design to be checked for *overturning,* and require calculations for *torsion.* If severe *configuration irregularities* are present, the *Provisions* require that a more complex analysis be used instead of the simple equivalent lateral force procedure. There are, of

---

SAMPLE CALCULATION
(simple equation):

$$V = C_s W \text{ and } C_s = 2.5A_a/R$$

For San Francisco:
  A_a = 0.40 (map)

For steel moment frame:
  R = 8.0 (Table 3.3)

For URM:
  R = 1.25 (Table 3.3)

Then:

For steel moment frame:
  C_s = 2.5 X 0.40/8 = 0.0125 (12.5% "G")

For URM:
  C_s = 2.5 X 0.40/1.25 = 0.80 (80% "G")

Figure 5.4

Eric Elsesser

Figure 5.5: Executive Order 12699 requires adoption of seismic standards in the design of all new buildings used, purchased or constructed with Federal assistance. The purpose is to avoid failures, such as that pictured above and opposite, and to reduce risks to occupants.

course many other issues presented in the *Provisions* that are not reflected in this simplified presentation. Nevertheless, the essence of any seismic code philosophy resides in the equivalent lateral force formula, and its relationship to the basic principles that have been discussed can readily be seen.

PERFORMANCE OBJECTIVES

One issue currently the focus of considerable effort is that of attempting to define performance objectives for seismic design, and ultimately to embody these in guidelines and codes. Performance objectives are statements of the limits of damage which a structure will be expected to sustain when subjected to specified earthquake demands, expressed in terms of defined ground motion. Performance objectives are expressed in terms of the performance of both the structural and nonstructural components.

The Guidelines for the Seismic Rehabilitation of Buildings, now under development by the Building Seismic Safety Council, defines three performance levels. Collapse Prevention requires that all significant components of the gravity load-resisting system must continue to carry their demands, although significant risk of injury due to falling hazards may exist. Life Safety requires that, while considerable structural damage may have occurred, major structural and nonstructural components have not become dislodged, creating a threat to life: the risk of life-threatening injury is very low. Immediate Occupancy is a damage state in which only very limited damage may have occurred. Nonstructural damage is minimized such that basic access and life safety systems including doors, elevators, emergency lighting, fire alarms, and suppression systems remain operable if power is available. Minor clean-up could be required.

While the specific terms for these damage states, and others, may change as work on this document proceeds, the philosophy of recognizing the inevitability of damage is characteristic of all the current focus on performance.

PRESIDENTIAL EXECUTIVE ORDER

An important development in the nationwide regulation of seismic building standards was the enactment into law in January 1990 of Executive Order 12699. This order requires that methods be taken to *reduce risks to the lives of occupants of buildings leased for federal uses or purchased or constructed with federal assistance, to reduce risks to the lives of persons who would be affected by engineering failures of federally assisted or regulated buildings, and to protect public investments, all in a cost-effective manner.*

The order directed federal agencies to issue regulations or procedures by February 1993 that incorporate seismic safety measures for all federal buildings that are owned, leased, assisted, or regulated by the federal government.

The link between seismic safety requirements and the availability of federal funds for new building construction was expected to encourage local governments and private sector building designers and contractors to update their codes and practices. (Figures 5.5, 5.6 and 5.7)

The order applies to any building located worldwide which is federally owned, lease constructed, leased (15 % or more of total space), regulated or financially assisted. This includes new construction financed with federal grants or loans, or federally insured or guaranteed loans or mortgages.

Individual federal agencies must ensure that building construction under their programs complies with the Executive Order. The Interagency Committee on Seismic Safety in Construction (ICSSC), which is a committee of federal agencies, recommends the use of seismic design and construction standards and practices equivalent to or exceeding those in the most recent (or immediately preceding) edition of the *NEHRP Provisions*.

The ICSSC determined that the following model building codes, including local codes that adopt and enforce these model codes in their entirety, are substantially equivalent to the *NEHRP Provisions*, and thus are appropriate for implementing the Executive Order.

- 1991 *Uniform Building Code* of the International Congress of Building Officials (ICBO)
- 1992 Supplement to the Building Officials and Code Administrators (BOCA) *National Building Code*, and
- 1992 Amendments to the Southern Building Code Congress (SBCCI) *Standard Building Code*.

Revisions of these model codes are considered appropriate for order implementation, as long as they are substantially equivalent to the latest version of the triennially published *NEHRP Provisions*. The order allows federal agencies to use local building codes if they, or the ICSSC, determine that the local codes provide adequately for seismic safety. Each federal agency must determine the steps that participants in its program must take to comply with the provisions of the Executive Order. FEMA has the responsibility of reporting every two years to the President and Congress on the execution of the order.

The implications of this Executive Order are far-reaching. In effect, the federal government is taking a leadership role in earthquake hazard mitigation by insisting that its own buildings, whether owned, leased or assisted, meet appropriate seismic standards. The results of the Executive Order will be watched with interest. Under normal rates of construction and retirement of buildings, a large proportion of federal buildings will be seismically resistant in 25 years.

Figures 5.6 and 5.7

Chapter 6: Nonstructural Damage

INTRODUCTION

To the engineer, nonstructural components are those that are not part of the structural system of the building. (Figure 6.2) For seismic design purposes, these are commonly categorized as:

- Architectural components,
- Mechanical and electrical components, and
- Building contents and equipment.

Code requirements for seismic design are currently aimed primarily at life safety, which is interpreted in engineering terms as ensuring against structural collapse. However, damage to nonstructural components may also cause casualties, even if the structure meets its design objectives. Perhaps of more significance is that nonstructural damage is the cause of much economic loss and its repair may leave the building unusable for weeks or months. Thus the problems of casualties, economic loss, and loss of building use must be alleviated by seismic design of the structure and the nonstructural components and by protection of the building contents.

While seismic design in general has made enormous strides in the last few decades, it is still true that, even in a well-designed and constructed building, freedom from earthquake damage cannot be guaranteed. (Figure 6.1) This was proven again in the 1994 Northridge, California quake, where nonstructural damage costs ranged into the hundreds of millions of dollars. Even if the building structure is undamaged and the occupants are safe and unharmed, substantial amounts of nonstructural damage must be expected unless special steps are taken to eliminate it.

THE PROBLEM

Four types of safety hazards presented by nonstructural components are:

- Direct hazard - the possibility of casualties because of broken glass, light fixtures, appendages, etc.,
- Loss of critical function - casualties caused by loss of power to hospital life support systems in bed panels, or functional loss to fire, police or emergency service facilities,
- Release of hazardous materials - casualties caused by release of toxic chemicals, drugs, or radioactive materials and,
- Fire caused by nonstructural damage - damage to gas lines, electrical disruption, etc.

Figure 6.1: This fluorescent fixture is supported by its conduit, and remains illuminated.

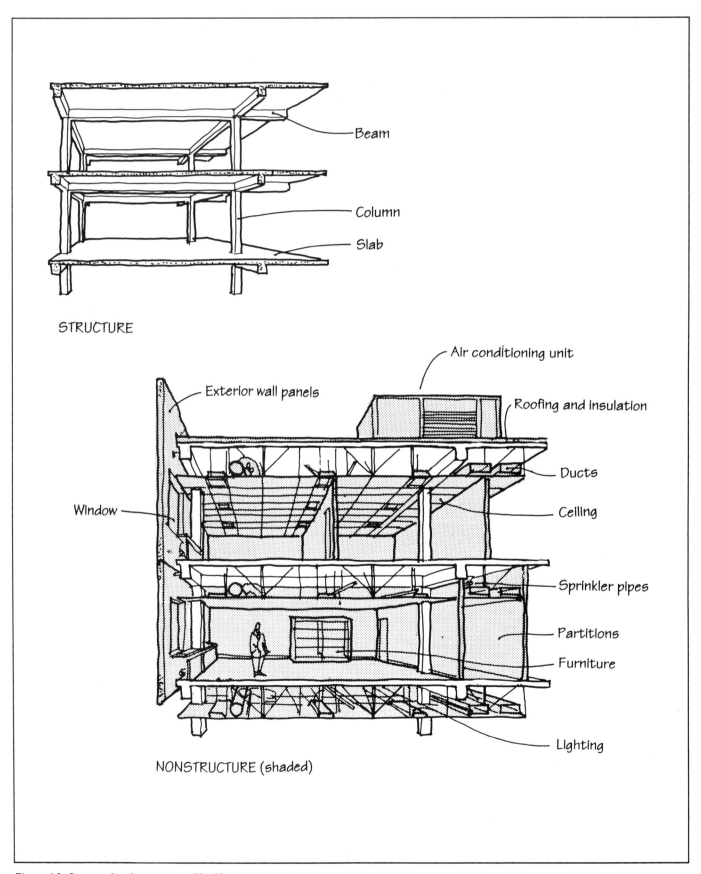

STRUCTURE

Beam

Column

Slab

Air conditioning unit

Exterior wall panels

Roofing and insulation

Window

Ducts

Ceiling

Sprinkler pipes

Partitions

Furniture

Lighting

NONSTRUCTURE (shaded)

Figure 6.2: Structural and nonstructural building components

Although these hazards have all caused loss of life and injuries in earthquakes, the number of deaths and serious injuries has been very low and suggestive more of random chance than a significant pattern of cause and effect. However, the possibility of heavy casualties, whether from a toxic spill, major glass breakage, or any other low probability damage, suggests that the life safety threat of nonstructural components should not be discounted.

Seismic codes and guidelines broadly define a group of nonstructural components as life safety hazards and provide criteria and design requirements aimed at reducing the hazard.

Economic Loss

Economic loss refers to the direct cost of repairing nonstructural damage. Statistical information on this cost is lacking, but experience in recent earthquakes indicates that the aggregate losses are very high. While these losses are primarily the result of a small amount of damage to a large number of buildings - damage to gypsum board partitions, suspended ceilings, and architectural finishes - some buildings also sustain nonstructural losses that are extremely costly to repair. (Figure 6.3) Ceiling and sprinkler damage to the San Francisco Airport in the 1989 Loma Prieta earthquake amounted to several million dollars.

The value of the nonstructural components in a building may be as high as 80-90% of the total costs in a complex facility such as a hospital or as low as 20 - 30% in an industrial or storage building with low system costs and minimal architectural features. Building contents values may be minimal in a partially occupied speculative office building, or many times the value in a building with expensive equipment or inventories.

Loss of Building Function

Nonstructural damage may cause loss of building function for a period of time, even in a building with little or no structural damage. (Figure 6.4) Loss of function may be the result of damage to components or systems necessary for useful function such as power and plumbing systems, or it may be due to disruption created by the repair of architectural or other nonstructural components. Prolonged disruption of function is generally the result of the need to repair both structural and nonstructural damage. Functional loss through system failure, in the absence of structural damage, tends to be short lived -a few days only- but for critical emergency facilities, function during this time period is essential for their post-earthquake role.

Structural Response Modification

One important aspect of the seismic design problem is that, while certain components are defined as nonstructural, nature may not repect the definition. Nonstructural components may modify the designed structural response in ways detrimental to the safety of the building. Examples are: placing heavy nonstructural partitions in locations that result in severe torsion and stress concentration, or placement of nonstructural partitions between columns in

Figure 6.3: Dangerous and costly ceiling damage to a banking floor in Managua, Nicaragua, 1972

Figure 6.4: Nonstructural damage can be very costly to repair and can cause loss of building function.

Figure 6.5: Heavy nonstructural block walls inserted into this frame have caused a short column condition, and subsequent column failure.

Figure 6.6: This roof-top mechanical unit jumped off its support and fractured its gas supply line.

Figure 6.7: Cladding falling from this store in the 1964 Alaska earthquake killed two people.

such a way as to produce a short column condition. (Figure 6.5) This can lead to column failure, distortion and further nonstructural or structural damage. Additional problems occur when these offending nonstructural elements are added during the building occupancy and are not subject to structural evaluation.

The Causes of Nonstructural Damage

In general, nonstructural damage is caused in two ways: *acceleration* or *displacement*. In acceleration related damage a nonstructural component is directly affected by ground motion transmitted by the main structure of the building and is subject to accelerations and consequent inertial forces in a similar way to the building structure. Thus, a roof-top mechanical unit may respond to the high accelerations at the top of the building by displacing several inches and breaking its supply piping in the process. (Figure 6.6)

Alternatively, components or equipment may be affected by displacement - movement or distortion in the structural elements that support or abut the elements. Thus, tile facing falls from a supporting wall because of the wall racking or a glazing element fails because of distortion in the supporting structure.

TYPICAL NONSTRUCTURAL DAMAGE

Architectural Components

Typical damage to architectural components is as follows:

1) Exterior Cladding

Experience has shown that rigid clip-angle connections for heavy concrete panels, commonly used in the lower seismic regions of the U.S., (Figure 6.7) do not ensure safe performance. In California, special seismic details have been developed in cladding and its connections. Little cladding damage was caused in the Loma Prieta and Northridge earthquakes, but many buildings were at the threshold where spalling would occur.

Unreinforced masonry filler walls, often used as solid party walls or as interior partitions, suffer severe damage and may also modify the performance of the structural frame. These may provide beneficial stiffening and prevent collapse, or, if irregularly placed, may cause local stress concentrations and lead to severe damage or collapse. Many examples of both these phenomena occurred in Mexico City (1985).

Glass and metal curtain walls depend primarily on maintaining clearances between glass and metal to accommodate movement caused by building drift. Performance in moderate earthquakes in the United States has been good, and in Mexico City (1985) performance was good even in the most intense damage zones although building response was such that curtain walls on taller buildings were probably not severely tested. Performance of curtain walls for large U.S.

Christopher Arnold

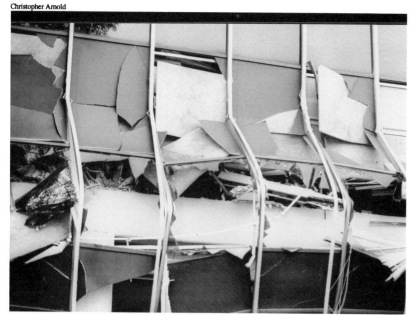

Figure 6.9: Nonstructural partitions can be damaged by distortion of the main structure.

Figure 6.8: Pancaking of the concrete floor in this medical building at Northridge in 1994 caused extreme distortion in the metal curtain wall.

Figure 6.10: Fallen light fixtures and ceiling make this exit corridor unusable, and the building non-functional.

earthquakes remains a matter of concern. Curtain walls cannot be detailed to accommodate extreme structural distortion. (Figure 6.8) Storefront glazing was shown to be particularly vulnerable in the Northridge earthquake.

2) Partitions

Generally, non-load bearing partitions are damaged by racking, caused by deflection or permanent distortion of the main structure. Architectural finishes, such as ceramic tile, frequently drop off the nonstructural backing. Unreinforced unit masonry or hollow tile partitions (usually found in older buildings) are very prone to damage. (Figure 6.9)

3) Suspended Ceilings

Older suspended ceiling systems have no positive attachments between elements of the system: tee-bars spread or pull away from wall support, and performance has been poor. (Figure 6.10) The performance of very large suspended ceiling systems, used in open plan offices, is largely untested. However, considerable damage was caused in the Loma Prieta and Northridge earthquakes to these systems.

4) Appendages and Parapets

Appendages, such as signs or large cornices located high on a building are subject to great accelerations, and their failure may cause casualties and additional damage to their own or surrounding buildings. Weak unreinforced masonry parapets have caused numerous deaths and injuries in recent U.S. earthquakes.

Figure 6.11: Collapse of heavy concrete canopy trapped ambulance in the 1971 San Fernando earthquake

Figure 6.12: Typical residential chimney failure, Northridge, 1994

Figure 6.13: Stairs made impassible by debris from adjoining nonstructural wall

5) Canopies and Marquees

Modern free-standing canopies - at building entrances or elsewhere - sometimes perform badly. At Olive View Hospital in San Fernando (1971) exits were blocked by collapsed canopies and a free-standing shelter collapsed on a number of ambulances, trapping them. (Figure 6.11) Many canopies also failed in Mexico City (1985). These elements are defined as nonstructural for seismic purposes because they are not part of the building lateral force resisting system, but they may be part of the building structure or designed as free-standing structural elements, and are usually subject to engineering design.

6) Chimneys and Stacks

Brick chimneys are vulnerable to damage, and could cause casualties: sometimes they fall through roofs and cause additional structural damage. (Figure 6.12)

7) Means of Egress and Access

Means of egress and access are of particular concern, because evacuation of a damaged building after an earthquake may be an important safety precaution, and the egress route should be clear of obstruction. The same routes should be available to rescue and inspection personnel entering the building. Besides the structural integrity of the building, egress routes should have protected ceilings, partitions and stairway enclosures.

Staircases, which are defined as nonstructural if they are structurally independent of the building structure, are critical elements in egress design, and their integrity is essential for building evacuation. In Olive View hospital, the four independent stair towers at the building corners overturned and were unusable.

Experience in Alaska (1964), San Fernando (1971), and a number of foreign earthquakes has shown that even a small amount of nonstructural damage - to either the stairs or their surroundings - may make the stair useless or dangerous when it is most needed. (Figure 6.13) Experience has also shown that nonstructural staircase enclosures of hollow tile or concrete block are particularly prone to fracture and render the stairs dangerous or unusable.

The structural interactions of stairway enclosures with the main structure of the building need to be more closely analyzed and designed. Although stairs are often designed as nonstructural, they frequently end up playing an unintentional structural role by acting as stiffening braces which, depending on their locations, can cause severe torsion and be detrimental to structural performance.

Mechanical and Electrical Components

Mechanical and plumbing components have seldom formed a life threat in themselves, but fire suppression plumbing may be critical because damage to gas lines, electrical disruption, etc. have been frequent causes of fires. However, recorded casualties in modern earthquakes are few.

Figure 6.14: Heavy mechanical distribution components have ripped through the ceiling of this showroom.

Figure 6.15: Inoperable chiller, San Fernando earthquake, 1971

It is not difficult to greatly improve the seismic performance of these systems for new buildings, but many existing buildings - including hospitals - retain vulnerable systems that are difficult to upgrade unless done as part of general rehabilitation. Also, these systems are complex, and a failure in any part may shutdown the whole system.

1) Mechanical Components

Mechanical equipment is often heavy, resulting in large inertial forces. (Figures 6.14 and 6.15) If securely attached, damage is greatly reduced. Piping systems generally perform well, but points of connection to equipment are vulnerable. Mechanical damage is expensive to repair because the equipment is costly, access is often difficult, and labor costs are high. (Figure 6.16)

2) Plumbing Components

Plumbing distribution systems usually have a fair amount of flexibility to withstand shaking. If anchored to ensure that they move with the structure, and if differential movement at joints is restricted, performance is good. However, sustained shaking will discover any weak links in the system. (Figure 6.17)

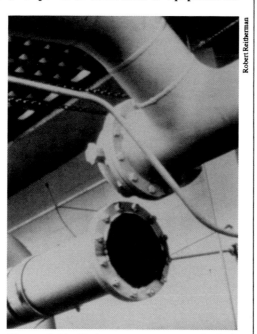

Figure 6.17: Piping systems are particularly vulnerable at joints and connections.

Figure 6.16: Mechanical equipment is unserviceable.

Figure 6.18: Elevators can be highly vulnerable to earthquake shaking.

Figure 6.19: Telephone equipment torn apart in the San Fernando earthquake, 1971

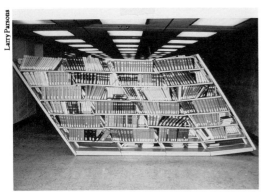

Figure 6.20: Shelving has proven to be particularly vulnerable to damage.

3) Elevators

All recent earthquakes have shown elevators to be highly vulnerable to damage during earthquakes. (Figure 6.18) The car and counterweight can derail within the guide rail assembly. The entire guide rail assembly can separate from the structure. Travel cables can become entangled in the hoistway. Swinging counterweights can crash through hoistway walls or sever the travel cables. Control and generator assemblies can overturn, and door and frame assemblies can fail. As a result of experience, improved design standards and details have been recommended and in some cases mandated, such as in the California Hospital Act. However, even short-term stoppage of elevators - if only for inspection - creates major functional problems, particularly in hospitals. Observed damage to elevators underscores the need for earthquake-resistant stair design to provide an alternative route.

4) Electrical Components

Electrical equipment in general is not a common safety threat, although dangerous fires have been caused by electrical failures, but emergency power components need protection, and emergency lighting should be secure. In certain building occupancies casualties may be caused by loss of a critical functional system, such as power to hospital life support systems in an intensive care unit or to fire, police or emergency service facilities. For example, two people in intensive care at the Olive View hospital were killed when power failed in the 1971 San Fernando earthquake.

Heavy equipment such as switchgears, transformers, and batteries are the most vulnerable parts of the system. Emergency systems are usually dependent on batteries, which must be securely installed. Emergency power systems dependent on oil or natural gas may be vulnerable to pipeline damage.

5) Communication Equipment

Telephone systems have proved to be vulnerable because of the immediate increase in the number of calls after an earthquake: performance of hardware and distribution systems is generally good, although individual subsystems can fail. (Figure 6.19)

Computer-backed data processing systems have increased enormously in complexity and importance since the San Fernando earthquake. Most large companies in the San Francisco Bay Area and Los Angeles, for whom data safety is critical, now employ back-up data saving systems in off-site locations.

Building Contents: Furniture and Equipment

Little systematic quantitative data is available on the extent to which building contents are damaged or destroyed in earthquakes. The problem was identified more thoroughly after the 1964 Alaska earthquake and after San Fernando (1971). Library shelving, with its heavy loading, has proved to be particularly vulnerable (Figures 6.20), as has office equipment. (Figure 6.21)

The contents and equipment in stiff structures, typically reinforced concrete shear-wall buildings, suffer far less damage than those in more flexible, frame-type buildings. This point was dramatically exemplified by the difference in nonstructural damage between the Banco Central (frame) building, which experienced severe nonstructural and contents damage and the Banco de America (shear wall) building, which had minor nonstructural and contents damage, in Managua (1972).

The Morgan Hill (1984) and Mt. Lewis (1986) earthquakes resulted in considerable contents and work station damage in the steel moment frame of the Santa Clara County Services Building, though no other structural or nonstructural damage occurred. (Figure 6.22) Heavy shelves that were braced following the first earthquake performed very well in the second.

Though there is clear potential for injury, there is as yet little conclusive evidence that many serious casualties are directly caused by office furniture. Self-protective actions, either instructive or trained, seem to be effective.

Some items of contents or equipment, such as heavy industrial machinery, may represent a life threat, but this is not generally within the responsibility of the building designer unless it is installed as part of the initial building fitting-out. Spillage of toxic materials may present a problem, while tall storage racks are included in most seismic codes as a potential falling hazard.

It is now understood that the ability of manufacturing plants to resume operation may depend more on damage to contents and equipment than on damage to the building. If the equipment is intact and power is available, production can resume under temporary walls and roofs.

It is clear from the Loma Prieta and Northridge experiences that earthquakes result in universal contents upset in all buildings. At a conservative estimate, in these earthquakes, several *million* people experienced toppled and displaced shelves, books, ornaments and equipment, together with frightening noise and motion, in their homes and places of work. Although as seismic designers we may dismiss contents upset as inconsequential (compared to collapse), to the building occupant it is a terrifying and traumatic experience.

It is also clear that contents upset (except in specific cases where careful mitigation action has been taken) must be regarded as an inevitable post-earthquake nuisance: it cannot be eliminated. (Figure 6.23) Building occupants must understand what is going to happen, be encouraged to take self protective measures, and be prepared to pick up the mess. Moreover, present designs for gypsum board partitions and hung ceilings must be regarded as replaceable components, and the occasional earthquake is similar in its effect to the occasional tenant remodel.

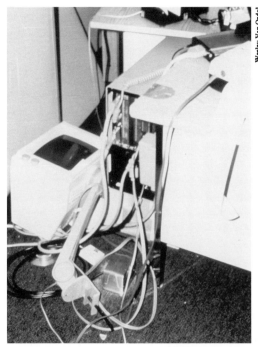

Figure 6.21: Desk-top equipment can easily be lost, even in a minor earthquake.

Figure 6.22: Damage to a workstation, Santa Clara County Services Building, Morgan Hill earthquake, 1984. There was no structural damage to the building.

Figure 6.23: Chemical spill in a school lab during the 1971 San Fernando earthquake

Figure 6.24: File cabinets act like tall slender buildings and are subject to overturning due to inertial forces.

Figure 6.25: Distortion in the building structure caused the entry door to this interior office to jam, trapping the single occupant. The jagged hole was made by rescue workers, cutting through the gypsum board.

Figure 6.26: This mixing box is laterally braced. Wire clusters hanging from the structure are used to brace the ceiling grid.

REDUCING NONSTRUCTURAL DAMAGE

Methods of reducing the damage to nonstructural components must be directed towards the probable modes of failure, whether through inertial forces (Figure 6.24) or distortion in backing or abutting structures. (Figure 6.25) For inertial forces, nonstructural components must be designed in a similar way to the building structure, using an analysis of forces to determine the loads on the component or its anchorage or bracing. To accommodate distortion, separation from back-up or abutting structures is necessary. Cladding must be designed to allow for movement of supporting frames, and heavy nonstructural walls must be detached from enclosing structure to allow for differential movement.

Mechanical, electrical, and plumbing distribution systems must be secured to the building structure (Figure 6.26) - with allowance for differential movement where applicable - such as where systems cross a seismic separation joint.

Most seismic codes deal with nonstructural components in a limited way and, in general, emphasize the first kind of failure mode noted above, that of inertial forces due to ground motion. Thus, both the UBC and the NEHRP Provisions provide seismic coefficients which, applied in a simple formula, result in an equivalent static force analogous to the base shear of the equivalent lateral force analysis for the building structure.

By way of example, some of the requirements for nonstructural components that are expressed in the 1991 *NEHRP Recommended Provisions* for new buildings are reproduced in Figure 6.27.

Minimum design levels for architectural, mechanical and electrical systems and components are established in Chapter 8 of the *NEHRP Provisions*. These design levels recognize occupancy use, occupant load, the need for operational continuity, and the interrelationship of structural, mechanical and electrical systems.

Performance criteria of nonstructural components are listed in Table C8-1, in the *Provisions Commentary* (Volume II) wherein three levels of performance (superior, good, low) are defined. These levels of performance, in turn, are related to each component and the three seismic hazard exposure groups. Table 8.2.2 (Figure 6.27) provides seismic coefficients (C_c) and performance characteristic levels for architectural components. Additional tables provide similar data for mechanical and electrical components.

TABLE 8.2.2
Architectural Component Seismic Coefficient (C_c) and Performance Criteria Factor (P)[a]

Architectural Component	Component Seismic Coefficient (C_c)	Performance Criteria Factor (P) Seismic Hazard Exposure Group		
		I	II	III
Exterior nonbearing walls	0.9	1.5[d]	1.5[b]	1.5
Interior nonbearing walls				
Stair enclosures	1.5	1.0	1.0[c]	1.5
Elevator shaft enclosures	1.5	0.5[c]	0.5[c]	1.5
Other vertical shaft enclosures	0.9	1.0	1.0	1.5
Other nonbearing walls	0.9	1.0	1.0	1.5
Cantilever elements				
Parapets, chimneys, or stacks	3.0	1.5	1.5	1.5
Wall attachments (see Sec. 8.2.3)	3.0	1.5[d]	1.5[b]	1.5
Veneer connections	3.0	0.5	1.0[g]	1.0
Penthouses	0.6	NR	1.0	1.0
Structural fireproofing	0.9	0.5[f]	1.0[c]	1.5
Ceilings				
Fire-rated membrane	0.9	1.0	1.0	1.5
Nonfire-rated membrane	0.6	0.5	1.0	1.0
Storage racks more than 8 feet in height (contents included)	1.5	1.0	1.0	1.5
Access floors (supported equipment included)	2.0	0.5	1.0	1.5
Elevator and counterweight guiderails and supports	1.25	1.0	1.0	1.5
Appendages				
Roofing units	0.6	NR	1.0[b]	1.0
Containers and miscellaneous components (free standing)	1.5	NR	1.0	1.0
Partitions				
Horizontal exits including ceilings	0.9	1.0	1.5	1.5
Public corridors	0.9	0.5	1.0	1.5
Private corridors	0.6	NR	0.5	1.5
Full height area separation partitions	0.9	1.0	1.0	1.5
Full height other partitions	0.6	0.5	0.5	1.5
Partial height partitions	0.6	NR	0.5	1.0

NR = Not required

[a] See Sec. 8.1 for exceptions.
[b] P may be reduced by 0.5 if the area facing the exterior wall is normally inaccessible for a distance of 10 feet and the building is only 1 story.
[c] P shall be increased by 0.5 if the building is more than four stories or 40 feet in height.
[d] P shall be increased by 0.5 if the area facing the exterior wall is normally accessible within a distance of 10 ft. plus 1 ft. for each floor height.
[e] P may be reduced to NR if the building is less than 40 feet in height.
[f] P shall be increased by 0.5 for an occupancy containing flammable gases, liquids, or dust.
[g] P may be reduced by 0.5 if the area facing the exterior wall is normally inaccessible for a distance of 10 ft. plus 1 f.t of each floor of height.

Figure 6.27: Table 8.2.2 of the Provisions

Architectural components and their means of attachment shall be designed for seismic forces (F_p) determined in accordance with the following equation:

$$F_p = A_v C_c P W_c$$

where

F_p = the seismic force applied to a component of a building or equipment at its center of gravity

A_v = the seismic coefficient representing the effective peak velocity-related acceleration (obtained from map)

C_c = the seismic coefficient for architectural components, obtained from table in the Provisions

P = the performance criteria obtained from table in the Provisions

W_c = the weight of the architectural component

Figure 6.28

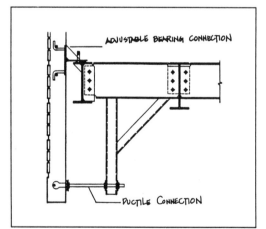

Figure 6.29

Through use of these tables, the design force F_p, for each nonstructural component, can be derived. The equation for the force F_p is shown in Figure 6.28. An explanation of the rationale behind these procedures is provided in Chapter 8 of Part 2, Commentary to the *NEHRP Recommended Provisions*. It must be recognized that the current philosophy of the seismic code not only accepts nonstructural damage but in fact mandates it. The implications of this philosophy have been expressed by Porush[*].

"Society's emphasis on protecting the lives of its citizens and, more importantly, the fact that code design does *not* specifically prevent damage is evident from the fact that building code design of structures presumes ductile inelastic (post-yield) behavior. Post-yield behavior in structural elements, by its very nature, implies that damage is being suffered in the form of cracking, permanent deformation, etc. Such behavior is not only tolerated, but encouraged as the optimum means of absorbing and dissipating the energy imparted to a structure by a major earthquake."

DESIGN AND/OR SELECTION RESPONSIBILITY

The nonstructural damage problem is particularly difficult to deal with because the nonstructural components subject to seismic forces are not normally within the design scope of the structural engineer, whose responsibility is typically confined to the design of the building structure. In addition, nonstructural components - such as partition walls - are often added after the initial building design, and the original architect, or any architect at all, is often not involved. Finally, nonstructural equipment and furnishings are generally selected by those uninvolved in the building design.

DESIGN FOR NONSTRUCTURAL DAMAGE REDUCTION

This section shows conceptual examples of design details for a number of typical nonstructural components. These are intended to give an indication of appropriate design approaches and should not be used as construction documentation.

1. Precast Concrete Cladding

This detail (Figure 6.29) shows typical "push-pull" connections for precast concrete cladding. The top connection provides bearing; the bottom connection uses a steel rod that will bend under lateral load and not transmit racking forces to the panel. The rod must be strong enough, however, to resist axial wind forces.

[*] Alan Porush. 1991. An Overview of the Development of Current Code Requirements for Nonstructural Elements. ATC-29, Applied Technology Council. Redwood City, CA.

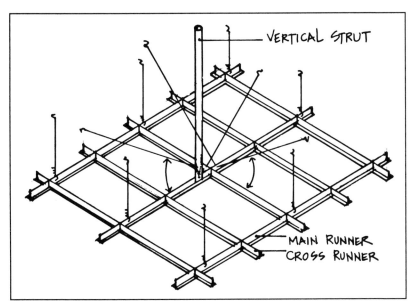

Figure 6.30

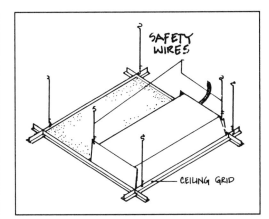

Figure 6.31

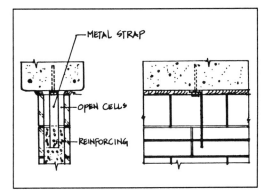

Figure 6.32

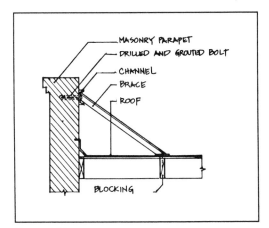

Figure 6.33

2. Suspended Ceilings

Typical suspended ceiling bracing. (Figure 6.30) Diagonal bracing by wires or rigid members: spacing should not be greater than 12'-0" x 12'-0". The vertical strut is recommended for large ceiling areas in high seismic risk zones. It may be provided by a piece of metal conduit, or metal angle section.

3. Light Fixtures

Heavy fluorescent light fixtures in suspended ceilings must be supported independently, so that if the grid fails the fixture will remain. Figure 6.31 shows a lighting fixture weighing less than 56 pounds, with two safety wires. For fixtures weighing more than 56 pounds, safety wires must be provided at all four corners. Suspended fixtures should be free to swing.

4. Heavy Partitions

Heavy partitions - such as concrete block - should be separated from surrounding structure to avoid stiffening the structure and to avoid transmitting racking forces into the partition. In Figure 6.32, the flexible steel strap resists out-of-plane forces but allows the structure to drift without imparting forces to the wall.

5. Parapet Bracing

Heavy parapets should be braced back to the roof structure. This is a typical problem with unreinforced masonry buildings, which often have large unsupported parapets. Figure 6.33 shows bracing for an existing masonry parapet: the roof should also be tied to the wall (not shown).

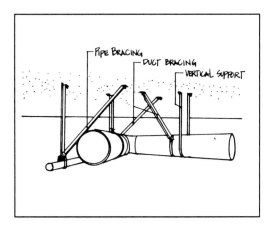

Figure 6.35

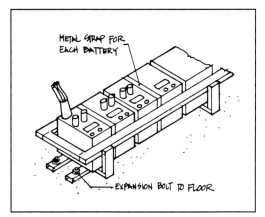

Figure 6.36

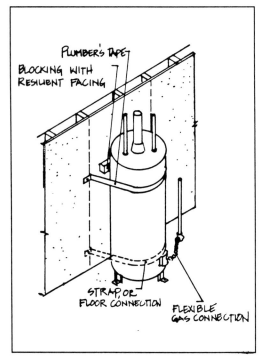

Figure 6.37

6. Tall Shelving

Tall shelves, such as library shelves, are heavily loaded and acceleration sensitive. They need longitudinal bracing and attachment to the floor. The top bracing should be attached to the building structure, and strong enough to resist buckling when the heavy shelves attempt to overturn. (Figure 6.34)

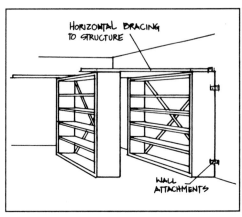

Figure 6.34

7. Mechanical Ductwork and Piping

HVAC duct work typically performs well in earthquakes, if correctly installed. (Figure 6.35) The sketch shows typical bracing for sheet metal ducts over 28" in diameter. Vertical support can be by straps or a metal angle. Heavy piping needs to be braced also.

8. Emergency Power Battery Racks

Batteries for emergency power need positive restraint. Figure 6.36 shows a custom designed rack, constructed from steel sections, to support and restrain a set of batteries. The batteries are also strapped to the rack for positive restraint. Alternative emergency power sources, such as gas or oil, need flexible utility connections and restrained equipment.

9. Gas Water Heaters

Domestic gas water heaters need restraint to prevent the heater tank from toppling and breaking the gas connection. (Figure 6.37) A flexible gas connection is desirable but not essential if the tank is well restrained. The bottom restraint can be provided by an additional strap, or by securely bolting the base supports to the floor.

10. Desk-top Equipment

Light equipment, such as computer monitors, can be restrained with "velcro" type devices. These provide good lateral restraint, but do not prevent easy relocation. (Figure 6.38)

11. Hazardous Material Containers

Materials such as oxygen tanks need positive restraint. Dangerous or essential bottled supplies can be placed in enclosed shelves or restrained by spring loaded wires to provide easy accessibility. (Figures 6.39 and 6.40)

Figure 6.38:"Velcro" type fasteners for this monitor hold it firmly against lateral forces, but it can easily be removed and relocated.

INTERIOR NONSTRUCTURAL HAZARD ASSESSMENT

It is useful to perform an assessment of interior hazards around the work place and public areas. The California Office of Emergency Services (OES) Earthquake Program publication, *Checklist of Nonstructural Earthquake Hazards*, provides a method of surveying an existing building to determine the level of hazard posed by nonstructural elements and contents. The FEMA Publication Number 74: *Protecting Your Home and Business from Nonstructural Damage* provides necessary information to do this, and also provides the necessary forms for organizing the assessment.

The California OES publication, *Identification and Reduction of Nonstructural Earthquake Hazards in California Schools*, provides a basis for identifying nonstructural hazards for schools, and illustrates conceptual ways of mitigating the hazards. Most of these hazards are common to all types of commercial, institutional and industrial buildings, in all parts of the country.

Figures 6.39 and 6.40: Pressurized tanks need to be securely restrained at top and bottom or they can topple.

Chapter 7: Seismic Rehabilitation of Existing Buildings

EXISTING STRUCTURES

Until recently research and design approaches to improving the performance of structures and efforts to upgrade building code provisions have focused on new buildings.

Over the last ten years a growing concern about the seismic performance of older buildings has arisen as it is realized that by far the greater hazard in major, damaging earthquakes is represented by older buildings still in use today but designed under previous code standards. (Figure 7.1) New construction conforming to the most current seismic codes only accounts for an addition of 2% per year to the total national building stock.

Seismic criteria for new buildings are generally inappropriate for use with old buildings; they are either too expensive or technically unworkable. As a consequence, several jurisdictions have relaxed the requirements for rehabilitation of existing buildings relative to new buildings. Notable is the City of Los Angeles Section 88 Code, and the California Historic Building Code (Title 8), both of which provide for reduced design forces and increased material stresses as applied to unreinforced masonry buildings, a major hazardous structural type. Currently, several projects are underway that will provide criteria and standards for the retrofit of existing buildings.*

The primary goal of seismic rehabilitation is to provide for life safety by minimizing the collapse exposure. Damage control and property protection are of secondary importance; an exception being historic structures where protection of the fabric or contents are also important, or other buildings such as museums and industrial buildings housing valuable or expensive contents. In addition, rehabilitation of essential facilities such as fire and police stations and hospitals may go far beyond life safety goals.

Christopher Arnold

Figure 7.1: Older buildings, not designed to recent seismic code provisions, can suffer serious damage in earthquakes.

---

* FEMA is currently sponsoring a major project that will provide a national set of guidelines for the rehabilitation of a variety of existing building types located in a number of different seismic zones in the U.S. Los Angeles has developed a set of criteria for rehabilitating tilt-up buildings and, following the Northridge earthquake, has adopted an ordinance that requires owners to rehabilitate their buildings.

HAZARDOUS BUILDING TYPES

Typically the hazardous types of existing construction are those with brittle, non-ductile assemblies. **Table 7.A** lists seven common types of construction that have been observed to fail in earthquakes. Unreinforced masonry bearing wall buildings with poorly tied floor and roof framing lack integrity and stability and usually fail by wall-collapse in out-of-plane motion. Non-ductile concrete frames are subject to sudden shear failure of the weak, unconfined columns. Steel diagonally braced structures can suffer non-ductile fracture of the braces or connections. Frame structures with architectural or "accidental" infill, above an open first floor can behave as soft-story structures with inadequate capacity. Failure of these hazardous buildings tends to be dramatic.

Table 7.A

SEISMIC REHABILITATION CONCEPTS FOR EXISTING BUILDINGS

Type of Structure	Add Strength	Alter Stiffness (and Response)	Add Continuity	Add Containment	Rationalize Capacity	Isolate
1. Timber Frame, Wood Floors	Add bracing	Steel or timber bracing	Add connection plates	Buttress	Ultimte capacity of timber	----
2. Unreinforced masonry, wood floors	Add R/C walls Add steel braces	Add R/C walls	Add chords + collectors	Add wall thickness gunite Add wall ribs Add steel basket Buttress	Ultimate capacity of URM (same configuration)	Low base isolate potential
3. Under-reinforced concrete walls, R/C floors	Thicken walls Add steel braces	----	Add chords + collectors	Buttress	----	Base isolate potential with large building
4. Non-ductile concrete frame, R/C floors	Add capacity to frame	Add R/C infill walls	----	Confine frame members Buttress	---	Base isolate potential with large building
5. Non-ductile nominal steel frame, R/C floors	Add steel bracing Strengthen steel frame	Add bracing	----	----	----	----
6. Non-ductile steel frame with infill walls R/C floors	Replace walls with R/C or braces	Remove and replace walls	----	Add wall ribs or thickness	Ultimate capacity of infill walls	Base isolate potential
7. Prestressed concrete slabs with R/C walls	Add R/C walls Add steel braces	----	----	----	----	Low base isolate potential

METHODS OF REHABILITATION

Strengthening of existing construction requires an understanding of both the old materials and the new reinforced elements. Added strength alone is not sufficient to ensure seismic stability. Figure 7.2 illustrates the compatibility problem between existing and new construction. The brittle masonry wall is not strong but is very rigid whereas a steel brace to reinforce the wall may have adequate strength but insufficient stiffness to overcome the rigidity of the masonry wall. The brace will be ineffective until the masonry cracks and distorts sufficiently for the lateral load to be transferred to the new element. Will this accomplish the intended goal? Not if property protection and damage control is desired; but it may, if preventing total collapse is the only goal. In contrast, the non-ductile flexible concrete frame is easily satisfied by the addition of a strong, rigid concrete shear wall.

Numerous concepts have been developed for strengthening existing construction; several have been tabulated in **Table 7.A**. The fundamental concepts are to 1) add strength, 2) alter stiffness, 3) add continuity, 4) add containment, 5) rationalize the existing capacity, and 6) isolate the building from the ground.

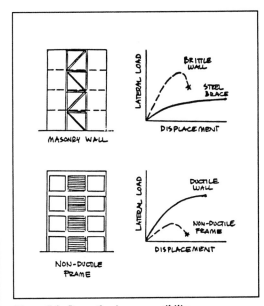

Figure 7.2: Strengthening compatibility

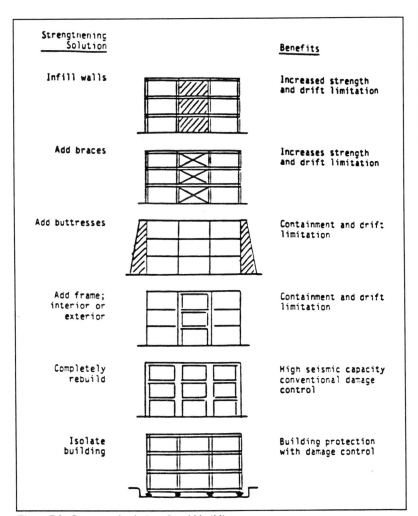

Figure 7.3: Conceptual solutions for old buildings

Figure 7.4: Historic State building, Sacramento, California

Figure 7.5: External steel bracing added to lift-slab government office building

Each of these concepts can be applied to individual constructions with varying degrees of success. Figure 7.3 illustrates some generalized solutions for old historic structures, with the corresponding benefits of each.

Besides structural issues, architectural concerns influence the solution. For historic buildings, such as the early twentieth century state building shown (Figure 7.4), rehabilitation measures must be devised that respect the original building architecture. For other buildings this may not be necessary, and affordable cost, safety and preservation of building function may be the paramount objectives. (Figure 7.5) The university administration building shown (Figure 7.6) is a non-ductile reinforced concrete frame building constructed in the 1960's. Rehabilitation consisted of strengthening the first floor columns and adding a perimeter steel frame. This solution enabled continued occupancy of the building while construction work proceeded; architecturally, the result is, arguably, a more interesting building.

Figure 7.6: External bracing added to university administration building

Base isolation is coming into increasing use for the rehabilitation of historic structures. The first such building to be rehabilitated was the City and County building in Salt Lake City (Figure 7.7), using a system of steel and rubber bearings inserted in the building crawl space (Figure 7.8). The same system is being used in the repair and rehabilitation of the Oakland City Hall, severely damaged in the Loma Prieta earthquake of 1989. A large federal building in San Francisco is currently being rehabilitated using a system of bearings that consist of pivots riding freely within a concave steel "cup". (Figure 7.9)

The advantage of using base isolation for these buildings is that the reduction in forces transmitted to the building superstructure reduces the amount of costly, and possibly damaging, structural changes and additions within the building. Base isolation systems can also provide assurance of greatly reduced nonstructural and contents damage relative to fixed-base systems.

The basic principles of seismic design apply equally to existing and new buildings. However, the designer working on an existing building is faced with a number of given conditions - of configuration, material, structural system, and detail - that are probably substandard and could be a significant threat to life. The problem then becomes one of augmenting or replacing those elements of the existing structural system that are inadequate, or in some way reducing the forces on the building so that the existing system can be equal to the task. This is a relatively new design problem and there is by no means universal agreement on the best methods of upgrading the range of hazardous existing buildings. However, from the experience of communities like Santa Cruz, during the 1989 California earthquake, it is clear that earthquakes will "find" the structural weaknesses in existing buildings, no matter what forms of "cosmetic" upgrades have been applied. The results for such seemingly new and refurbished structures can be catastrophic.

Figure 7.7: The City and County building in Salt Lake City is now base-isolated.

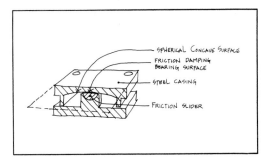

Figure 7.9: Friction pendulum type bearing

Figure 7.8: Crawl space in City and County building. The black block is a rubber and steel bearing. The existing concrete supports to the left and in foreground will be removed when all bearings are in place.

Chapter 8: Seismic Design Process

ROLES AND RESPONSIBILITIES

As the member of the design team who initiates the design concept and develops it through design development and construction documentation, the architect can play a key role in the seismic design process. In the traditional design process the architect also plays a coordinating role among the other design professionals, and serves as the voice of the design team to the client. While other design and construction processes, such as design/build and some types of construction management, may change the authority of the architect's position, his role as concept designer remains. To ensure that consideration of seismic issues occurs with the right degree of priority - and at the right time in the design process - the architect needs to have a clear conceptual understanding of seismic design issues, at least to the level outlined in this publication.

While the structural engineer must play a major role in providing an earthquake-resistant design, the overall design responsibility is shared between architect and engineer, because of architectural decisions that impact the seismic design. Architects cannot delegate seismic design wholly to the engineer. (Figure 8.1)

Even before design begins there are issues of desired seismic performance, expectations related to different anticipated earthquake levels, and cost-benefit analysis that an informed architect must discuss with his client, or other members of the design team, to ensure that the client's expectations are clear and the design objectives understood. (Figure 8.2)

The issue of desired seismic performance relates to the fact that damage-free seismic performance cannot be guaranteed. Building codes are designed to ensure life-safety, but not to prevent damage, and the client should be informed of this fact in the beginning of the design process. A higher level of seismic design *can* reduce probable damage, but there are additional design and construction costs associated with this. Depending on the nature of the building, and the level of seismic hazard, these additional costs may be justified, but, as in many other aspects of the design, it is the architect's job to explain the available alternatives as clearly and accurately as possible, and let the client make the decision.

The fact that alternative levels of building performance can be defined and to some extent, chosen, is a relatively new development in seismic design. Some of its origin lies in the performance of buildings in recent earthquakes, in which owners whose buildings suffered damage in the hundreds of thousands of dollars, or even more, were surprised to hear that their building met the intents

Christopher Arnold

Figure 8.1: Ensuring building performance is the shared responsibility of architects, engineers and other members of the building team.

Paul Neel, FAIA

Figure 8.2: The architect/engineer team must interact effectively from the beginning of the design process. Lack of communication can result in costly and sometimes disastrous consequences.

Christopher Arnold

Figure 8.3: To participate optimally in a building team, architects must have a basic understanding of how seismic forces move through buildings and what good design can do to resist them.

of the seismic code, since no one was killed or injured. Out of these experiences came the realization among the design professionals, of the need to be more explicit about what seismic design could, and could not, accomplish.

One practical result of these new understandings was the need to reinforce the recommendation that the architect and engineer work together from the inception of a design project, and discuss issues of desired or expected performance before conceptual design begins. The idea of engineer participation in early design concepts is not new, yet often it does not happen, for a variety of economic, cultural and professional reasons. If they are to work effectively together the owner, architect, and engineer must be able to communicate using a shared language within a common conceptual framework.

CHECKLISTS FOR COORDINATION

A recent committee of the California State Seismic Safety Commission*, in looking at the architect's role in earthquake hazard mitigation, suggested that the use of common guidelines and checklists that highlight key seismic design issues needing resolution could greatly facilitate communication within owner-architect-engineer teams.

The use of the following Check Lists was proposed.

Check List No. 1 takes the form of a charting of design expectations that can enable design-team members and owners to agree on seismic goals that are reasonably in line with resources available. Agreement on such goals and expectations can help achieve a desired level of performance and limit later

*Committee on Architect's Role in Earthquake Hazard Mitigation, Seismic Safety Commission, State of California, Sacramento, CA. 1992.

surprises due to unexpected earthquake damage. Such a statement might properly be part of a project's building program documents.

Currently, the definition of levels of performance and the setting of objectives is the subject of a number of studies, including a FEMA Study of *Performance-Based Seismic Design of Buildings*. This study is being undertaken by a team from the Earthquake Engineering Research Center, University of California, Berkeley, and is intended to lead to an action plan for problem-focused studies on topics such as overall performance, analysis and design methods, risk assessment and structural reliability, and implementation of the new standards and codes that might be developed.

Check List No. 2 lists a number of technical items that should be discussed and resolved between architect and engineer. If the architect does not understand any of the listed items, the engineer should explain. Similarly, if planning or other constraints force the architect into less than optimum seismic configurations or other characteristics, the use of this check list will ensure their identification early in the design process.

Check List No. 3 relates to agreement and scope of work among the major consultants and suppliers. Costs and a competitive market tend to limit the time available for design. Working within limited budgets and time, architects and engineers, while following customary practice, may nevertheless leave some design tasks to engineers employed by contractors or vendors (e.g. precast cladding panels, stairs and elevators). At times this can reduce building quality and performance to levels that may be less than desirable with respect to seismic safety and leave the designers open to possible litigation.

Scope-of-work agreements can be based on guidelines such as those shown in Check List No. 3. An example of how such a list might be filled in is shown in **Check List No. 4**.

Use of such guidelines in negotiating agreements may assist design professionals in their efforts to convince owners that providing for modest additional amounts of professional time during design may yield large dividends in the long run. Scope-of-work agreements can also be valuable tools for architects in defining and coordinating the roles of the design and construction team.

Constantly evolving seismic codes do not relieve the architect from responsibility for understanding the essential concepts of good earthquake design. If architects are to remain design leaders and coordinators they must understand the technical concepts involved. Recent large projects to repair and upgrade buildings damaged in the 1989 Loma Prieta earthquake in California have placed the prime design role in the hands of the structural engineer, with the architect relegated to a subsidiary consultant position. As increasing attention is paid to seismic design, this situation could become more frequent, unless the architect can show that his or her knowledge and guidance is essential to the efficient working of the design and construction team. (Figures 8.3 and 8.4)

Christopher Arnold

Figure 8.4

Checklist No. 1

Seismic Expectations

A. Earthquake Performance of Structure

Earthquake	Damage			
	No life threat, collapse	Repairable Damage: evacuation	Repairable Damage: no evacuation	No Significant Damage
Low-Moderate				
Mod-Large				
Large				

B. Earthquake Performance of Nonstructural Components

Earthquake	Damage			
	No life threat. failures	Repairable Damage: evacuation	Repairable Damage: no evacuation	No Significant Damage
Low-Moderate				
Mod-Large				
Large				

C. Function Continuance: Structural/Nonstructural

Earthquake	Time to Reoccupy			
	6 months +	To 3 months	To 2 weeks	Immediate
Low-Moderate				
Mod-Large				
Large				

Notes: Earthquakes
Low-Moderate: up to Richter M 6.5
Moderate-Large: Richter M 6.5 - 7.5
Large: Richter M 7.5+

Classification may be modified by poor soil conditions or specific seismological forecasts.

Checklist No. 2   **Checklist to Facilitate Architect/Engineer Interaction**

Item	Minor Issue	Major Issue	Significant Issue
Goals			
Life Safety			
Damage Control			
Continued Function			
Site Characteristics			
Near Fault			
Ground Failure Possibility			
(landslide, liquefaction)			
Soft Soil (amplification, long period)			
Building Configuration			
Height			
Size Effects			
Architectural Concept			
Core Location			
Stair Locations			
Vertical Discontinuity			
Soft Story			
Set Back			
Offset Resistance elements			
Plan Discontinuity			
Re-entrant Corner			
Eccentric Mass			
Adjacency-Pounding possibility			
Structural System			
Dynamic Resonance			
Diaphragm Integrity			
Torsion			
Redundancy			
Deformation Compatibility			
Out-of-Plane Vibration			
Unbalanced Resistance			
Resistance Location			
Drift/Interstory Effect			
Stong Column/Weak Beam condition			
Structural System			
Ductility			
Inelastic Demand Constant or Degrading			
Damping			
Energy Dissipation Capacity			
Yield/Fracture Behavior			
Special System (e.g., base isolation)			
Mixed System			
Repairability			
Nonstructural Components			
Cladding, glazing			
Deform. Compatability			
Mounting System			
Random Infill			
Ceiling Attachment			
Partition Attachment			
Rigid			
Floating			
Replaceable Partitions			
Stairs			
Rigid			
Detached			
Elevators			
MEP Equipment			
Special Equipment			
Computer/Communications equipment			

Discussion of all significant issues:

Checklist No. 3

DESIGN SCOPE-OF-WORK GUIDELINES

Item	Design	Coordinate	Check	Shop Dwgs	Sign/Stamp	Field Review
Foundation						
Super Structure						
Steel Frame						
Concrete Frame						
Precast or Post-Tensioned Floors						
Open Web Joists						
Cladding						
Precast, Stone						
Metal						
Glass						
Stairs						
Elevator						
Ceilings						
Equipment						
MEP Systems						

*This table represents a hypothetical project and should not be taken as a suggestion for assigning specific responsibilities, which must be uniquely established for each project.

Key:

A =   Architect
SE =   Structural Engineer
MEP =   Mechanical, Electrical, Plumbing Consultant
V =   Vendor, subcontractor or manufacturer of manufactured, assembled or prefabricated components or systems
G =   Geotechnical Engineer

Checklist No. 4

DESIGN SCOPE-OF-WORK GUIDELINES

Item	Activity					
	Design	Coordinate	Check	Shop Dwgs	Sign/Stamp	Field Review
Foundation	SE	A	G	SE	SE	A, SE
Super Structure						
Steel Frame	SE	A	SE	SE	SE	SE
Concrete Frame	SE	A	SE	SE	SE	SE
Precast or Post-Tensioned Floors	V	SE	SE	SE	V, SE	SE
Open Web Joists	V	SE	SE	SE	V, SE	SE
Cladding						
Precast, Stone	V	A, SE	SE	SE	V	A, SE
Metal	V	A	SE	A	V	A
Glass	V	A	A	A	--	A
Stairs	A, SE, V	A	SE	SE	V, SE	A, SE
Elevator	V	A	SE	A, SE	V	A, SE
Ceilings	A	A	SE	A	A	A
Equipment	V	A	SE	A	V, SE	A, SE
MEP Systems	MEP	A	SE	MEP	MEP	MEP

*This table represents a hypothetical project and should not be taken as a suggestion for assigning specific responsibilities, which must be uniquely established for each project.

Key:

A =   Architect
SE =   Structural Engineer
MEP =   Mechanical, Electrical, Plumbing Consultant
V =   Vendor, Subcontractor or Manufacturer of manufactured, assembled or prefabricated components or systems
G =   Geotechnical Engineer

Chapter 9: The Planning Process

THE PLANNING PROCESS

In seismic design, each building and site lies within a broader context of regional seismicity, localized geology, community vulnerability, and adjacent structures and land uses. Many of these factors have traditionally been addressed by city planning, but each must be incorporated by the designer in the architectural development of a seismically resistant building.

City and regional planning policies and regulations play a significant role in both, providing for the orderly growth, development, governance and maintenance of communities. They also play a major role in influencing architectural decisions affecting seismic safety.

The authority to plan a community is derived from the most basic powers of government: the *police powers* to protect the health, safety and welfare of a community. The authority to establish zoning districts and regulations, regulate and separate land uses, provide adequate infrastructure, and ensure safety against natural and manmade hazards is derived from this same responsibility to ensure *health, safety, and public welfare.*

The planning profession's evolution from the physical design of buildings to the physical design of cities has more recently evolved to a more comprehensive definition of planning that includes concerns that range from the development of long-range land-use plans, the regulation of height, bulk and density of development and the provision of infrastructure, to the maintenance of the historical, cultural and economic vitality of cities.

Until recently a concern for environmental and geological hazards was missing. Quite often, development was permitted in flood plains, in areas of active landslides, over or directly adjacent to active earthquake fault traces, and in areas that will shake the most violently in an earthquake.

The legacy of nearly two centuries of development decisions that disregarded seismic hazards, combined with the rapid growth of cities prior to 1970, has left many cities vulnerable to earthquake damage; and not just cities in California. Nearly every state in the Union has some vulnerability to earthquake threat as illustrated by a map of projected ground accelerations prepared by the United States Geological Survey. (Figure 9.1) The metropolitan regions of the Pacific Northwest, the Northeast, Southeast, and Central States all share California's vulnerability to earthquake damage. (Figure 9.2)

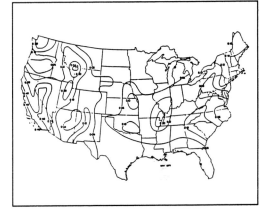

Figure 9.1

Many communities have yet to adopt a seismic building code to regulate construction, let alone regulate development based on seismic criteria. It is sobering to note that the effects of a repeat of the 1811-12 New Madrid earthquakes would be devastating to cities in the Midwest (within the states of Missouri, Indiana, Kentucky, Tennessee, Illinois, Arkansas and Mississippi) where seismic building regulations are just now being adopted.

The key decision-maker responsible for providing seismic safety to our communities is the local government; the city or county. It is this level of government in the United States that establishes and administers building and planning policy and regulations.

A Comprehensive Planning Approach

Planning today is broadly defined to include a number of topics ranging from social policy to those subjects related to architectural practice. Topics include both those which address the physical structure of a community and those which relate to the social and economic fabric. Often, community planning is called upon to address existing social and economic inequities in a city, including economic decline, inadequate affordable housing, and de facto segregation. Traditionally, "comprehensive planning" was defined to include only those topics related to land use and transportation. It has today come to mean nearly every topic related to public safety, social equality and environmental quality.

Figure 9.2: The rapid growth of urban centers since the 1970s has left many cities throughout the U.S. and the world vulnerable to earthquake damage.

THE GENERAL PLAN

The key document of government policy in planning is the General Plan, usually consisting of statements concerning development and a General Plan map defining land uses and densities appropriate for different sections of the community. The Plan usually contains the following elements:

- Land Use
- Circulation
- Housing
- Conservation
- Open Space
- Noise.

SEISMIC SAFETY PLANNING

In the aftermath of the 1971 San Fernando earthquake the state of California required local governments to specifically identify their seismic vulnerability in their general Plans. The State now requires every jurisdiction to prepare a *Seismic Safety Element* of their general plan which identifies areas subject to faulting, ground failure, liquefaction, intense ground shaking and tsunami or dam failure inundation.

While all of the *Plan Elements* have relevance to a community's seismic safety, the *Seismic Safety Element* is intended to focus and interrelate issues of land use, housing, circulation and open space into a comprehensive set of policies and programs that address the overall safety of the community, *including the elimination of existing hazards*.

It is critical to recognize that planning and development decisions that appear inconsequential may impact the seismic performance of buildings and affect life safety. The irregular street pattern in Mexico City resulted in numerous triangular lots and buildings of triangular and otherwise irregular configuration. Zoning-based height limits often result in buildings being stepped back from the street, causing discontinuity of vertical configuration and stiffness. Narrow, congested streets fronted by multistory, masonry buildings can leave pedestrians and building occupants without a place of refuge during and after an earthquake - another negative result of the lack of community planning. All these factors derive from planning decisions and directly influence how individual buildings will perform.

Damage in the Loma Prieta earthquake (1989) was defined by areas where development was permitted on active landslides in the Santa Cruz Mountains, on hydraulically placed, non-engineered fills of San Francisco's Marina District, and in areas where ground shaking was intensified by local geology in Santa Cruz, Oakland and San Francisco. These factors, ignored during the planning and development decision making process, combined with archaic building construction to define the Loma Prieta earthquake disaster. The apparently inconsequential planning decisions of the 1920s, when develop-

Richard Chylinski

Figure 9.3: Damaged buildings can have dangerous and disruptive impacts well beyond the property line.

ment occurred in these areas, determined the outcome of an earthquake eighty years later.

Standards for subdivision and life-line design utilized at the turn of the century may create even greater risks to older urban communities. Until 1991, there had not been a major urban fire in the United States since the 1906 earthquake and fire which devastated San Francisco. The possibility of an earthquake-created conflagration had been discounted by planners, possibly because they had not been confronted by a conflagration from any cause for 8 decades. The East Bay Hills fire (Oakland-Berkeley Hills of October 1991) brought into focus the risk to older communities where land parcels are small, setbacks between structures minimal, streets widths narrow, and water systems inadequate to deliver more than the minimum standard. Within four hours, nearly 3,500 residences were consumed by the East Bay fire storm, leaving more than 8,000 homeless. Burning one house every 4 seconds, the fire proved unstoppable until nature, in the form of decreased winds and onshore fog, intervened. Where earthquake risk is significant, the potential for post earthquake fires is also real. New development in older communities, or changes of use that increase occupancy load, should be cautiously assessed in light of capacity of existing life line and safety systems essential to post-earthquake response.

URBAN DESIGN

The practice of urban design in American cities is shared by architects and planners. Urban designers address issues of building height and bulk, density, site coverage, architectural character, streetscape, the relationships of buildings and groups of buildings, historic preservation and the quality, quantity, and location of open spaces between buildings. Recent earthquakes have revealed that many of these urban design components can have critical impacts on building performance and community safety. Battering of adjacent buildings and the inadequate areas of refuge for evacuation and emergency shelter are but two examples of the potential problems that exist at the urban scale. (Figure 9.3)

The Coalinga (1983), Whittier (1987), Loma Prieta (1989), and Northridge (1994) earthquakes in California illustrated the folly of urban design without considerations of seismic risk. In each community, downtown redevelopment plans provided for major reinvestment in the central business district, facade beautification, streetscape treatment and new landscaping. Their redevelopment plans provided for beautification and densification without seismic strengthening. Unfortunately, "structural" paint was not strong enough to hold the bricks in place when the earth shook! (Figure 9.4)

Urban designers can address these issues within current practice through height limits, requirements for open space to provide for public shelters, emergency access, fire separation, streetscape design to protect pedestrians from debris falling from buildings, density transfer and historic district preservation to support strengthening existing structures, and maintaining low density occupancies in areas with numerous unreinforced masonry buildings.

PLANNING TO REDUCE SEISMIC RISK

Fault Zone Mapping

The initial step in making planning and land-use development decisions to reduce seismic risk is to identify and map active fault zones within a community. Geologists usually classify an active fault as one that has moved within the past 11,000 years. Recently active fault traces can be mapped from aerial photographs, maps of surface geology, and/or from field investigations. In the relatively young regions of the western United States, surface faulting can also be mapped. In the central and eastern United States, where faulting occurs several thousand feet below the surface without surface manifestations, fault mapping can be accomplished by mapping small earthquakes.

Where surface faulting is evident, fault rupture zones can be established by state or local law. Typically, fault zones are defined as 200 yards on either side of the fault trace. Within this zone, construction can be limited or occupancies restricted. In California, the State mandates Special Studies Zones on all known active fault traces. Before construction is permitted within a zone, the exact location of the fault trace must be established. No buildings can be constructed within 25 feet of the fault trace. These restrictions have effectively precluded the construction of new buildings on known fault traces. However, the law has not affected existing structures that were built in the fault zone prior to the passage of the Alquist-Priolo Special Studies Zone legislation.

SEISMIC ZONATION

A second planning approach to reducing seismic risk is to zone a community based on the potential for violent ground shaking or ground failure. Seismic risk maps based on surface geology and subsurface investigations such as well and coring records can provide a measure of relative risk upon which to base land use and development decisions. Seismic zonation, along with slope stability, landslide potential, flood plain and environmental sensitivity mapping can provide the basis for a "land capability analysis" to determine appropriate land use, density and occupancy levels.

These tools are not a substitute for investigations of a specific site to determine the suitability of a structural design. However, they do provide a community with an assessment of the relative risk to a site and should trigger more specific investigations.

Richard Chylinski

Figure 9.4: Downtown redevelopment plans in seismically hazardous areas must go beyond simple beautification and facade treatments.

Christopher Arnold

Figure 9.5: Hazardous buildings will impact adjacent areas and can cause damage to neighboring buildings and infrastructure.

INVENTORY EXISTING HAZARDOUS BUILDINGS AND MANDATED RETROFIT

The primary concern to public safety is damage or collapse of older structures built during a period when seismic codes either did not exist, we now realize, were inadequate to provide resistance to earthquake forces. Older wood frame structures, with unbraced cripple walls or without foundation anchor bolts to hold the structure to its foundation; unreinforced brick or masonry structures; and non-ductile concrete structures pose the greatest danger. The first-priority structures, because of their vulnerability to collapse and high occupancy residential and commercial uses, should be non-ductile concrete and unreinforced masonry.

The first step in developing a mitigation program is to prepare an inventory of these structures and to notify building owners of their potential danger. In California, the state has mandated that local governments develop such an inventory of unreinforced masonry buildings and institute a retrofit program that shall include notification. (SB 547, Chp. 250, Stat. 1986, California Government Code Sec. 8875 et seq.)

The second step in mitigation is to establish building code standards to govern the strengthening of buildings. There is continuing debate among researchers and practicing engineers to define the most appropriate methods and standards for the retrofit of existing structures. Currently the Uniform Code for Building Conservation (International Conference of Building Officials, Whittier, CA) provides guidance for the strengthening of unreinforced masonry construction. Drafts of standards and codes to address the retrofit of other types of structures are being developed by the Federal Emergency Management Agency (FEMA) and the Applied Technology Council (ATC). The issue of debate in establishing a standard for retrofit is the determination of the most cost effective standard of performance for a historic structural type. Traditionally, this standard has been set at a lower level of performance than that established for new construction, recognizing the cultural value to the community to preserving historic structures and that too high a standard would be cost prohibitive.

The strong tradition of local home rule in the United States has dictated that local governments, cities and counties, determine the type of retrofit program appropriate to their community. This has resulted in a broad range of approaches to retrofit that vary from jurisdiction to jurisdiction; from the restrictive to the laissez faire or non-existent. The question that should be addressed when undertaking the "upgrading" of a structure that lacks seismic resistance is whether the upgrading or change of occupancy increases the risk (population exposed to a collapse hazard) posed by the structure; and whether this new level of risk is acceptable. (Figures 9.5 and 9.6)

THE ARCHITECT'S ROLE IN DISASTER PREPAREDNESS, RESPONSE AND RECOVERY

Safety Assessment of Damaged Buildings -- CCAIA

Architects can participate in vital community response and recovery activities by working with local and state emergency services organizations in developing post-disaster safety assessment programs. A moderate or larger earthquake will produce widespread damage in an urban area. The rapid assessment of damage is a critical first step in emergency response and community recovery. In previous earthquakes, structural and civil engineers have assisted local government officials in surveying damaged structures to determine their safety. They were concerned with large, complex, high occupancy structures. After the 1987 Whitter earthquake, it took more than two months for the local building department to survey damage to residential structures to determine their safety. In most cases the structures were safe to reenter, but in many cases, residents were occupying structures where safety was uncertain. The 1989 Loma Prieta earthquake again overwhelmed local government's capability to quickly assess damage. For the first time, architect volunteers participated in safety assessment of damaged structures after a major earthquake.

To meet the demand to evaluate the large number of residential and commercial structures that would likely be damaged in future earthquakes, the San Mateo Chapter of the California Council of The American Institute of Architects (AIA) developed a prototype program to train architects in damage assessment. The program has been implemented in California, and fully integrated into the state's response planning.

Community Recovery and Reconstruction Design Assistance

For several years, The AIA's Regional/Urban Design Committee has assisted communities across the country by organizing Regional/Urban Design Assistance Teams (R/UDATs) to focus on issues of design, development and redevelopment. The work of the R/UDATs and similar efforts of components responded to the needs of communities after disasters, most notably floods in the southern and southeastern U.S. There was, however, no organized disaster response function within The AIA.

After the 1983 Coalinga earthquake, however, volunteers from the California Council of The American Institute of Architects (CCAIA) organized the California Emergency Design Assistance Team (CEDAT) and participated in a design charrette to develop alternative approaches to the reconstruction of Coalinga's devastated central business district. Assisted by students from the school of architecture at the California Polytechnic State University at San Luis Obispo, the CCAIA team worked with downtown merchants, community residents and city officials to create a vision to guide economic investment and rebuilding. Modeled on The AIA's R/UDAT, the CEDAT developed schemes to provide for the incremental and economic redevelopment of the community. The approach was adopted by Coalinga and provided the basis for their reconstruction planning.

Figure 9.6

A similar effort, initiated by members of the CCAIA after the Armenian earthquake of 1988 involved AIA members in a multinational design charrette with their Russian and Armenian counterparts to develop proposals for the reconstruction of Spitak. Following the 1989 Loma Prieta earthquake a CEDAT team organized a workshop in Santa Cruz to present ideas and options for the reconstruction of the destroyed downtown shopping district. In each of these examples, architects actively participated in the recovery and reconstruction of communities after disasters, providing volunteer resources that would not otherwise be available and contributing immeasurably to community recovery.

To support what had been an ad hoc response effort by individual architects or chapters, the Regional/Urban Design Committee developed and disseminated the *Disaster Response Guide for Components*, guidelines for component organizations for the provision of post-disaster design and planning assistance. The guidelines are available from AIA chapter offices or from The AIA national office.

Glossary of Terminology

Accelerogram - The record from an accelerograph showing acceleration as a function of time.

Accelerograph - A strong motion earthquake instrument recording accelerations.

Acceleration - Rate of change of velocity with time.

Aftershock - An earthquake, usually a member of an aftershock series often within the span of several months following the occurrence of a large earthquake (main shock). The magnitude of an aftershock is usually smaller than the main shock.

Amplification - A relative increase in ground motion between one type of soil and another, or an increase in building response as a result of resonance.

Amplitude - Maximum deviation from mean of the center line of a wave.

Base Isolation - A method whereby a building superstructure is detached from its foundation in order to change the characteristics of earthquake forces transmitted to the building.

Base Shear - Calculated total shear force acting at the base of a structure, used in codes as a static representation of lateral earthquake forces. Also referred to as "equivalent lateral force."

Brittle Failure - Failure in a material which generally has a very limited plastic range; material subject to sudden failure without warning.

Configuration:

  Building Configuration - The size, shape and geometric proportions of a building.

  Structural Configuration - The size, shape and arrangement of the vertical load carrying and lateral force resistant components of a building.

Damping - A rate at which natural vibration decays as a result of absorption of energy.

Deflection - The state of being turned aside from a straight line, generally used in the horizontal sense. See also drift.

Design Earthquake - In the NEHRP Provisions the earthquake that produces ground motions at the site under consideration that have a 90 percent probability of not being exceeded in 50 years (or a 10 percent probability of being exceeded). This is equivalent to a mean Return Period of 475 years, or an annual risk of 0.002 events a year.

Design Ground Motion - See Design Earthquake

Diaphragm - A horizontal or nearly horizontal structural element designed to transmit lateral forces to the vertical elements of the seismic resisting system.

Drift - Vertical deflection of a building or structure caused by lateral forces. See also Story Drift.

Ductility - Property of some materials, such as steel, to distort when subjected to forces while still retaining considerable strength.

Dynamic - Having to do with bodies in motion.

Effective Peak Acceleration and Effective Peak Velocity-Related Acceleration - Coefficients shown on maps in the NEHRP Provisions for determining prescribed seismic forces.

Elastic - The ability of a material to return to its original form and condition after a displacing force is removed.

Energy Absorption - Energy is absorbed as a structure distorts inelastically.

Energy Dissipation - Reduction in intensity of earthquake shock waves with time and distance, or by transmission through discontinuous materials with different absorption capabilities.

Epicenter - A point on the earth's surface which is directly above the focus of an earthquake.

Exceedance Probability - The probability that a specified level of ground motion or specified social or economic consequences of earthquakes will be exceeded at a site or in a region during a specified exposure time.

Exposure - The potential economic loss to all or certain subsets of the built environment as a result of one or more earthquakes in an area. This term usually refers to the insured value of structures carried by one or more insurers.

Failure Mode - The manner in which a structure fails (column buckling, overturning, etc.).

Fault - A fracture in the earth's crust accompanied by displacement of one side of the fracture with respect to the other and in a direction parallel to the fracture.

Normal Fault - A fault under tension where the overlying block moves down the dip or slope of the fault plane.

Strike-Slip Fault (or lateral slip) - A fault whose relative displacement is purely horizontal.

Thrust (Reverse) Fault - A fault under compression where the overlying block moves up the dip of the fault plane.

Oblique-Slip Fault - A combination of normal and slip or thrust and slip faults whose movement is diagonal along the dip of the fault plane.

Focus - The location of a fault break where an earthquake originates (also termed hypocenter).

Force - Agency or influence that tries to deform an object or overcome its resistance to motion.

Frames:

Braced Frame - One which is dependent upon diagonal braces for stability and capacity to resist lateral forces. In concentric braced frames, diagonal braces are arranged concentric to column/beam joints; in eccentric braced frames, they are eccentric.

Moment Frame - A space frame in which members and joints are capable of resisting lateral forces by bending as well as along the axis of the members. Varying levels of resistance are provided by Ordinary, Intermediate and Special Moment Frames as defined in the NEHRP Provisions with Special Frames providing the most resistance.

Frame, Space - A structural system composed of interconnected members, other than bearing walls, that is capable of supporting vertical loads and that may also provide resistance to seismic forces.

Frequency - Referring to vibrations; the number of wave peaks which pass through a point in a unit of time, usually measured in cycles per second.

Fundamental Period - See "Period."

"G" - The acceleration due to gravity, or 32 feet per second.

Ground Failure - Physical changes to the ground surface produced by an earthquake, such as lateral spreading, landslides or liquefaction.

Hypocenter - See Focus.

Inelastic - The inability of a material to return to its original form and condition after a displacing force is removed; permanent distortion.

Intensity - A subjective measure of the force of an earthquake at a particular place as measured by its effects on persons, structures and earth materials. Intensity is a measure of energy. The principal scale used in the United States today is the Modified Mercalli, 1956 version.

Irregular - Deviation of a building configuration from a simple symmetrical shape.

Lateral Force Coefficients - Factors applied to the weight of a structure or its parts to determine lateral forces for seismic design.

Liquefaction - Transformation of a granular material (soil) from a solid state into a liquified state as a consequence of increased pore-water pressure induced by vibration.

Loss - Any adverse economic or social consequences caused by earthquakes.

Mass - A constant quantity or aggregate of matter: the inertia or sluggishness which an object, when frictionlessly mounted, exhibits in response to any effort made to start it or stop it, or to change in any way its state of motion.

Mercalli Index (or Scale) - See "Intensity."

Microzone (microzonation) - Seismic zoning, generally by use of maps, for land areas smaller than regions shown in typical seismic code maps, but larger than individual building sites.

Modal Analysis - Determination of seismic design forces based upon the theoretical response of a structure to excitation in its several modes of vibration.

Nonstructural Components - Those building components which are not intended primarily for structural support and bracing of the building.

Out of Phase - The state where a structure in motion is not at the same frequency as the ground motion or an adjoining structure, or where equipment in a building vibrates at a different frequency from the structure.

P-Wave - See "Waves, Seismic."

Period - The elapsed time (generally in seconds) of a single cycle of a vibratory motion or oscillation: the inverse of frequency.

Recurrence Interval - See Return Period.

Resonance - The amplification of a vibratory motion occurring when the period of an impulse or periodic stimulus coincides with the period of the oscillating body.

Return Period (normally *mean* return period) - The time period in years in which the probability is 63 percent that an earthquake of a certain magnitude will recur.

Richter Magnitude (or Scale) - A measure of earthquake size which is determined by taking the common logarithm (base 10) of the largest ground motion recorded during the arrival of a P-wave or seismic surface wave and applying a standard correction for distance to the epicenter. The scale is named after its creator, American seismologist Charles R. Richter.

Rigidity - Relative stiffness of a structure or element. In numerical terms, equal to the reciprocal of displacement caused by unit force.

Risk - See "Seismic Risk."

S-Wave - See "Waves, Seismic."

Seiche - A standing wave on the surface of water in an enclosed or semi-enclosed basin (pool, lake, bay or harbor).

Seismic - Of, subject to, or caused by an earthquake or an earth vibration.

Seismic Event - The abrupt release of energy in the earth's lithosphere causing an earth vibration: an earthquake.

Seismic Forces - The actual forces created by earthquake motion; or assumed forces prescribed in the NEHRP Provisions or other codes, that are used in the seismic design of a building and its components.

Seismic Hazard - Any physical phenomenon such as ground shaking or ground failure associated with an earthquake that may produce adverse effects on the built environment and human activities: also, the probability of earthquakes of defined magnitude or intensity affecting a given location.

Seismic Hazard Exposure Group - A classification assigned in the NEHRP Provisions to a building based on its occupancy and use.

Seismic Performance Category - A classification assigned in the NEHRP Provisions to a building based on its Seismic Hazard Exposure Group and its Seismic Hazard.

Seismic Resisting System - The part of the structural system that is designed to provide required resistance to prescribed seismic forces.

Seismic Risk - The probability that the social or economic consequences of an earthquake will equal or exceed specified values at a site during a specified exposure time: in general, seismic risk is vulnerability multiplied by the seismic hazard.

Seismic Waves - See Waves, Seismic

Seismic Zone - Generally, areas defined on a map within which seismic design requirements are constant. In the NEHRP Provisions, seismic zones are defined both by contour lines and county boundaries.

Shear - A force which acts by attempting to cause the fibers, or planes, of an object to slide over one another.

Shear Panel - See Wall, Shear

Shear Wall - See Wall, Shear

Soil Structure Interaction - The effects of the properties of both soil and structure upon response of the structure.

Spectrum - A plot for a specific site indicating maximum earthquake response with respect to natural period or frequency of the structure or element. The response can be measured as acceleration, velocity, displacement or other properties.

Speed - Rate of change of distance travelled with time, irrespective of direction.

Stiffness - Resistance to deflection or drift of a structural component or system.

Story Drift - Vertical deflection of a single story of a building caused by lateral forces.

Strain - Deformation of a material per unit of the original dimension.

Strength - The capability of a material or structural member to resist or withstand applied forces.

Stress - Applied load per unit area, or internal resistance within a material that opposes a force's attempts to deform it.

System - An assembly of components or elements designed to perform a specific function, such as structural system.

Torque - The action of force that tends to produce torsion. The product of a force and lever arm, as in the action of using a wrench to tighten a nut.

Torsion - The twisting of a structural member about its longitudinal axis, or rotation of a building in plan about its center of resistance.

Tsunami - A sea wave produced by large area displacements of the ocean bottom, the result of earthquakes or volcanic eruptions.

Velocity - Rate of change of distance travelled with time in a given direction. In earthquakes, it usually refers to seismic waves and is expressed in inches or centimeters per second.

Vulnerability - The degree of loss to a given element at risk, or set of such elements, resulting from an earthquake of a given intensity or magnitude. Expressed in a scale ranging from no damage to total loss. A measure of the probability of damage to a structure or a number of structures.

Wall, Bearing - A wall providing support for vertical loads; it may be interior or exterior.

Wall, Nonbearing - A wall that does not provide support for vertical loads other than its own weight as permitted by the building code. It may be interior or exterior. Also, Partition.

Wall, Shear - A wall, bearing or nonbearing, designed to resist seismic forces acting in the plane of the wall.

Wall System, Bearing - A structural system with bearing walls providing support for all or major portions of the vertical loads. Seismic resistance may be provided by shear walls or braced frames.

Waves, Seismic - Vibrations in the form of waves created in the earth by an earthquake.

    Longitudinal Wave - Pure compressive wave with volume changes.

    Love Wave - Transverse vibration of seismic surface waves.

    P-Wave - The primary, or fastest waves travelling away from a fault rupture through the earth's crust, and consisting of a series of compressions and dilations of the ground material.

    Rayleigh Wave - Forward and vertical vibration of seismic surface waves.

    S-Wave - Shear, or secondary wave, produced essentially by the shearing or tearing motions of earthquakes at right angles to the direction of wave propagation.

    Seismic Surface Wave - A seismic wave that follows the earth's surface only, with a speed less than that of S-waves.

Weight - Name given, for practical purposes, to the mutual gravitational force between the earth and an object under consideration. Varies depending on distance of the object from the earth.

Selected References

AIA/ACSA Council on Architectural Research (1993). *"Nonstructural Seismic Damage: An Annotated Bibliography."* AIA/ACSA Research Council, Washington, DC.

Arnold, C. and Lagorio, H.J. (1987). *"Chinese City Starts Over After Quake."* In *Architecture*, pp. 83-85. American Institute of Architects (AIA), Washington, D.C.

Arnold, C. (1989). *"Mission to Armenia."* In *Architecture*, pp. 99-105. American Institute of Architects (AIA), Washington, D.C.

Arnold, C., and Reitherman, R. (1982). *Building Configuration and Seismic Design.* Wiley, New York.

Ayres, J.M., Sun, T., and Brown, F. (1973). *"Nonstructural Damage to Buildings."* In *The Great Alaska Earthquake of 1964*, pp. 346 - 456. National Academy of Sciences (NAS) and National Research Council (NRC), Washington, D.C.

Bay Area Regional Earthquake Preparedness Project (1990). *"An Ounce of Prevention."* In *NETWORKS: Earthquake Preparedness News,* Vol. 5, No. 2, California Office of Emergency Services Earthquake Program, Oakland, CA.

Bay Area Regional Earthquake Preparedness Project (1989). *Earthquake Vulnerability Analysis for Local Governments,* Special Report. California Office of Emergency Services Earthquake Program, Oakland, CA.

Bertero, Vitelmo, Ed. (1989). *Lessons Learned From the 1985 Mexico Earthquake.* Earthquake Engineering Research Institute (EERI), Oakland, CA.

Blair, M.L. (1979). *Seismic Safety and Land-Use Planning: Selected Examples from California. United States Geological Survey Professional Paper (U.S.)* 941-B

Bolt, B.A., Horn, W.L., et al. (1977). *Geological Hazards,* 2nd rev. ed. Springer-Verlag, New York.

Botsai, E.E., Eberhard, J.P., Lagorio, H.J. et al. (1976). *Architects and Earthquakes*. National Science Foundation and the AIA Research Corporation, Washington, D.C.

Building Seismic Safety Council (BSSC) (1988). *NEHRP Recommended Provisions for the Development of Seismic Regulations for New Buildings*. Federal Emergency Management Agency (FEMA), Washington, D.C.

Chopra, A.K. (1982). *Dynamics of Structures - A Primer*. Earthquake Engineering Research Institute (EERI), Oakland, CA.

Comerio, M., Friedman, H. and Lagorio, H.J. (1987). *Unreinforced Masonry Seismic Strengthening Workshop and Cost Analysis*. Center for Environmental Design Research (CEDR), University of California, Berkeley, and Center for Environmental Change (CEC), Inc., San Francisco.

Conner, H.W., Harris, J.R. et al. (1987). *Guide to Application of the NEHRP Recommended Provisions in the Earthquake-Resistant Building Design*. Federal Emergency Management Agency (FEMA), Washington, D.C. and Building Seismic Safety Council (BSSC), Washington, D.C.

Crawley, S.W., and Ward, D.B. (1990). *"Seismic and Wind Loads in Architectural Design: An Architect's Study Guide."* American Institute of Architects (AIA), Washington, D.C.

Department of Defense Tri-Services Seismic Design Committee (1982). *Technical Manual: Seismic Design for Buildings*. Departments of the Army, Navy, and the Air Force, Office of the Chief Engineers, Washington, D.C., for U.S. Army Division Engineer, South San Francisco, CA.

EERI Ad Hoc Committee on Seismic Performance (1994). *Expected Performance of Buildings*. Earthquake Engineering Research Institute (EERI), Oakland, CA.

Elsesser, E. (1984). "Life Hazards Created by Nonstructural Elements." In *Nonstructural Issues of Seismic Design and Construction*, Workshop Proceedings, pp. 27-36. Earthquake Engineering Research Institute (EERI), Oakland, CA.

Gallagher, R.P. Associates, Inc. (1989). *Procedures for Postearthquake Safety Evaluation of Building*. (ATC-20), Applied Technology Council (ATC), Redwood City, CA.

Geis, D.E., and Smith, K.N. (1989a). *Architectural and Urban Design Lessons from the 1985 Mexico City Earthquake*, AIA, Association of Collegiate Schools of Architecture (AIA/ACSA Research Council), Washington, D.C. and Colegio de Arquitectos de Mexico/Sociedad de Arquitectos Mexicanos, Mexico City.

Geis, D.E., and Smith, K.N. (1989b). *Designing for Earthquakes in Southern California.* AIA, Association of Collegiate Schools of Architecture (AIA/ACSA Research Council), Washington, D.C.

Governor's Office of Emergency Sercies, State of California and Federal Emergency Management Agency (1994). *A Guide to Repairing and Strengthening Your Home Before the Next Earthquake* OES California and FEMA, Oakland, CA.

HABITAT (United Nations Centre for Human Settlements) (1988). *Seismic Risk Management in the Planning of the Historic Center of Mexico City,* Project Monograph. HABITAT, Nairobi, Kenya.

Helfant, D.B. (1989). *Earthquake Safe: A Hazard Reduction Manual for Homes.* Builders Booksource Publication, Berkelely, CA.

Jacob, K.H. and Turkstra, C.J., Eds. (1989). *Earthquake Hazards and the Design of Constructed Facilites in the Eastern United States,* Annals of the New York Academy of Sciences, Volume 558. New York Academy of Sciences, New York, NY.

Jones, B.G. (1989). *The Need for a Dynamic Approach to Planning for Reconstruction After Earthquakes.* Department of Planning, Cornell University, Ithaca, NY.

Kessler, J.J. (1973b). *Summary and Conclusions for Hospitals and Medical Facilities,* Vol. 1, Part A, pp. 295-296. The San Fernando, California, Earthquake of February 9, 1971 National Oceanic and Atmospheric Administration (NOAA), Department of Commerce, Washington, D.C.

Lagorio, H.J. (1990). *Earthquakes: An Architect's Guide to Nonstructural Seismic Hazards.* John Wiley & Sons, Inc., New York.

Lagorio, H.J., Friedman, H., and Wong, K. (1986). *Issues for the Seismic Strengthening of Exisitng Buildings: A Practical Guide for Architects.* Center for Environmental Design Research (CEDR), University of California, Berkeley.

Lagorio, H.J. (1986). *Improving Seismic Safety: Urban Reconstruction Planning Following Earthquakes.* Center for Environmental Design Research (CEDR), University of California, Berkeley.

Luft, R.W. (1989). "Comparisons Among Earthquake Codes." In *Earthquake Spectra,* Vol. 5, No. 4, pp. 767-789. Earthquake Engineering Research Institute (EERI), Oakland, CA.

Mader, G.G. (1980). *Land Use Planning After Earthquakes.* William Spangle and Associates, Inc., Portola Valley, CA.

Mahin, S.A., Ed. (1984). *Fix' Em: Identification and Correction of Deficiencies in Earthquake Resistance of Existing Buildings.* Earthquake Engineering Research Institute (EERI), Oakland, CA.

Olson, R.A., et al. (1987). *Data Processing Facilities: Guidelines for Earthquake Hazards Mitigations.* VSP Associates, Inc., and FIMS, Inc., Sacramento, CA.

Reitherman, R.K. (1989). *"Significant Revisions in Model Seismic Code."* In *Architecture*, pp. 106-112. American Institute of Architects (AIA), Washington, D.C.

Scholl, R., Ed. (1982). *Reducing Earthquake Hazards Lessons Learned From Earthquakes.* Earthquake Engineering Research Institute (EERI), Oakland, CA.

Scholl, R., Lagorio, H.J., and Arnold, C. Eds. (1984). *Nonstructural Issues of Seismic Design and Construction*, Workshop Proceedings. Earthquake Engineering Research Institute (EERI), Oakland, CA.

Shapiro, Okino, Hom and Associates (1980). *The Homebuilder's Guide for Earthquake Design.* Applied Technology Council (ATC), Redwood City, CA.

Stratta, J.L. (1987). *Manual of Seismic Design.* Prentice-Hall, Englewood Cliffs, NJ.

Walker, B. and The Editors of Time-Life Books (1982). *Planet Earth: Earthquake.* Time-Life Books, Alexandria, VA.

Wiss, Janney, Elstner Associates, Inc. (1985). *Protecting Your Home and Business From Nonstructural Earthquake Damage.* State of California, Governor's Office of Emergency Services, Oakland, CA.

Yanev, Peter, I. (1974). *Peace of Mind in Earthquake Country: How to Save Your Home and Life.* Chronicle Books, San Francisco.

Federal Emergency Management Agency Publications

The Federal Emergency Management Agency (FEMA) is the lead agency responsible for overall planning and coordination of the National Earthquake Hazards Reduction Program, established by Congress in 1977. Other responsible agencies include the U.S. Geological Survey, the National Science Foundation, and the National Institute of Standards and Technology.

As part of its national efforts, FEMA has developed over 50 publicatons in its "Earthquake Hazards Reduction Series'" commonly known as the "Yellow Book" series. Among the titles of potential interest to practicing architects are the following:

Earthquake Hazard Reduction Series

Publication Number	Title	EHRS Number
FEMA 74	Protecting Your Home and Business From Nonstructural Earthquake Damage	EHRS #1
FEMA 77	The Planning Process (Brochure)	EHRS #11
FEMA 90	An Action Plan for Reducing Earthquake Hazards of Existing Buildings	EHRS #16
FEMA 95	NEHRP Recommended Provisions for the Development of Seismic Regulations for New Buildings Part I: Provisions & Maps (1991 Edition)	EHRS #17
FEMA 96	NEHRP Recommended Provisions for the Development of Seismic Regulations for New Buildings Part II: Commentary (1991 Edition)	EHRS #18
FEMA 99	Improving Seismic Safety of New Buildings: A Non-Technical Explanation of NEHRP Provisions	EHRS #20
FEMA 140	Guide to Application of the NEHRP Recommended Provisions in Earthquake-Resistant Building Design	EHRS #25
FEMA 146	Comprehensive Earthquake Preparedness Planning Guidelines: Large City	EHRS #33
FEMA 149	Seismic Considerations Elementary and Secondary Schools	EHRS #34
FEMA 150	Seismic Considerations Health Care Facilities	EHRS #35
FEMA 151	Seismic Considerations Hotels and Motels	EHRS #36
FEMA 152	Seismic Considerations Apartment Buildings	EHRS #37
FEMA 153	Seismic Considerations Office Buildings	EHRS #38
FEMA 154	Rapid Visual Screening of Buildings for Potential Seismic Hazards: A Handbook	EHRS #41
FEMA 156	Typical Costs for Seismic Rehabilitation of Existing Buildings Volume I - Summary	EHRS #39
FEMA 172	Techniques for Seismically Rehabilitating Existing Buildings	EHRS #49
FEMA 178	A Handbook for Seismic Evaluation of Existing Buildings	EHRS #47

Copies may be requested by writing to the following address:
Federal Emergency Management Agency, P.O. Box 70274, Washington, D.C. 20024.

Federal Emergency Management Agency Regional Offices

For further information on state and local FEMA activities with respect to the National Earthquake Hazards Reduction Program, please contact any of the regional offices listed below.

Region I (Boston)
442 J. W. McCormack POCH
Boston, MA 02109-4595
617-223-9540

Region II (New York)
26 Federal Plaza, Room 1337
New York, NY 10278-0002
212-225-7209

Region III (Philadelphia)
105 S. Seventh Street
Philadelphia, PA 19106-3316
215-931-5500

Region IV (Atlanta)
Suite 700, 1371 Peachtree Street, N.E.
Atlanta, GA 30309-3108
404-853-4200

Region V (Chicago)
175 West Jackson (4th Floor)
Chicago, IL 60604-2698
312-408-5500

Region VI (Dallas)
800 North Loop 288
Denton, TX 76201-3698
817-898-5104

Region VII (Kansas City)
911 Walnut Street, Room 200
Kansas City, MO 64106-2085
816-283-7061

Region VIII (Denver)
Denver Federal Center
Building 710, Box 25267
Denver, CO 80225-0267
303-235-4811

Region IX (San Francisco)
Building 105
Presidio of San Francisco
San Francisco, CA 94129-1250
415-923-7100

Region X (Seattle)
Federal Regional Center
130 228th Street, S.W.
Bothell, WA 98021-9796
206-481-8800

Additional Sources of Information

Applied Technology Council
555 Twin Dolphin Drive, Suite 550
Redwood City, CA 94065
Phone: 415-595-1542
Fax: 415-593-2320

Building Seismic Safety Council
1201 L Street, NW, Suite 400
Washington, DC 20005
Phone: 202-289-7800
Fax: 202-289-1092

California Office of Emergency Services Earthquake Program
101 8th St., Suite 152
Oakland, CA 94607
Phone: 510-540-2713
Fax: 510-540-3581

Earthquake Engineering Research Institute
499 14th Street, Suite 320
Oakland, CA 94612-1902
Phone: 510-451-0905
Fax: 510-451-5411

National Center for Earthquake Engineering Research
State University of New York at Buffalo
Red Jacket Quadrangle
Buffalo, NY 14261
Phone: 716-645-3391, Fax: 716-645-3399
e-mail: NERNCEER@UBVMS.BITNET

National Science Foundation
Bioengineering and Environmental Systems
4201 Wilson Blvd., Suite 565
Arlington, VA 22230
Phone: 703-306-1318
Fax: 703-306-0312

National Institute of Standards and Technology
Building and Fire Research
Gaithersburg, MD 20899
Phone: 301-975-5900
Fax: 301-975-4032

Seismic Safety Commission
State of California
1900 K. St., Suite 100
Sacramento, CA 95814
Phone: 916-322-4917
Fax: 916-322-9476

U.S. Geological Survey
12201 Sunrise Valley Drive
National Center
Reston, VA 22092
Phone: 703-648-6714
Fax: 703-648-6717

Index